P.P. B-99

CW00342418

A COLOUR GUIDE TO
BEETLES

A COLOUR GUIDE TO
BEETLES

by Svatopluk Bílý
Illustrated by Alena Čepická

TREASURE PRESS

Translated by Olga Kuthanová
Graphic design Miloš Lang
Designed and produced by Artia for
The Hamlyn Publishing Group Limited,
a division of the Octopus Publishing Group plc,
Michelin House, 81 Fulham Road
London SW3, 6RB

Copyright © 1990 Artia, Prague

All Rights Reserved.
No part of this publication may be reproduced or transmitted
in any form or by any means, electronic or mechanical,
including photocopying, recording or any information storage
and retrieval system, without permission in writing
from the copyright owner.

ISBN 1 85051 387 2

Printed in Czechoslovakia by Svoboda
3/15/24/51-01

CONTENTS

INTRODUCTION

Beetles (Coleoptera) are the largest order of the class of insects (Insecta). Some one million insect species have been described to date and further tens, if not hundreds of thousands, still await discovery. Insects are divided into approximately 29 orders, some of which include only several dozen known species, whereas in others, such as the Diptera, Hymenoptera and Lepidoptera, the number of described species may exceed one hundred thousand. Beetles are the largest order numbering some 400,000 known species to date — of these about 12,000 are found in Europe.

The diversity of shape, size and behaviour of beetles is enormous. This is due to their adaptation to widely different environments and their worldwide distribution. Beetles include dwarfs as well as veritable giants. The smallest of the family Ptiliidae are barely 0.5 mm long, whereas the largest giants of the family Cerambycidae measure almost 20 cm. The diversity in shape and coloration includes all the known colours, often in varied bright combinations.

Many beetles are of great economic importance to man, and some even rank among the most harmful of insect pests. For that reason their study is important. Environmental pollution is causing the disappearance of a great many species and several years from now some of the beetles that are presently quite common may be extinct. The vast diversity of beetles cannot be encompassed within the scope of this book, not even that of those native to Europe. Therefore it deals only with the most conspicuous and most important European species and the most important families of this interesting insect order. For those who are interested in more detailed information for studying the beetles of Europe we recommend two books which include all the beetle species of this area. They are *The Biology of the Coleoptera* by R. A. Crowson, published in 1981, and *A Field Guide to Beetles* by K. W. Harde, published in 1984 by Octopus.

MORPHOLOGY

The life cycle of beetles includes the following stages: egg, larva, pupa and the adult or imago.

The eggs of beetles are oval, ellipsoid, or very occasionally spherical. The outer layer, called the chorion, may be variously coloured, though it is generally white or creamy-white, and may be variously sculptured. It is usually composed of lipoproteins. This outer covering protects the contents of the egg, allows for the exchange of gases between the embryo and the external environment, and at the same

6

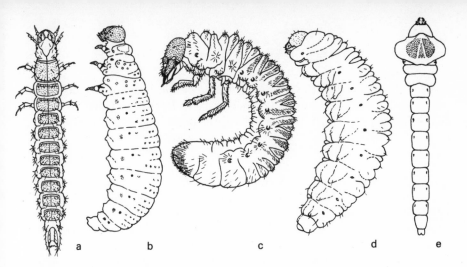

Beetle larvae: oligopod (a, b, c) and apodous (d, e); a, Carabidae;
b, Chrysomelidae; c, Scarabaeidae; d, Curculionidae; e, Buprestidae.

time prevents the egg from drying out. The egg contains yolk which
nourishes the developing embryo.

The eggs of beetles are generally laid singly or in small groups in
the ground or in the substrate on which the larvae feed. Sometimes
they are covered with a protective layer and in rare instances they
may be deposited in a special egg-case, a so-called cocoon (e.g. in
Hydrous piceus).

When the embryo has completed its development it emerges as
a larva. This larva passes through several developmental stages
known as the instars. The first instar larva usually bites through or
tears the outer egg with the aid of its so-called egg teeth, which are
generally located on the head and remain there throughout the duration of the first instar.

There are at least two instars in the development of the larva, but
usually more. The number of instars may be constant (e.g. in ground
beetles) or variable, depending on the quality of the food, the humidity and the temperature (e.g. buprestids and longhorn beetles).
Between each instar the larva moults. This is a very complex process
governed by hormones during which the old skin or cuticle is cast off
and replaced by a new one; the sloughed-off remnants are called
exuviae.

There are two types of beetle larvae: oligopod and apodous.
Oligopod larvae have well-formed thoracic limbs and abdominal
segments usualy without appendages, e.g. the larvae of lamellicorn
beetles, ground beetles, rove beetles, predacious diving beetles, ladybirds, etc. Apodous larvae have neither well-formed thoracic limbs

7

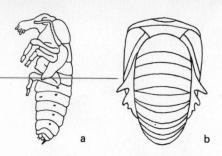

Types of beetle pupae:
a, exarate pupa — Curculionidae;
b, obtect pupa — Coccinellidae.

nor appendages on the abdominal segments, are generally coloured white, have a non-sclerotized body and often live inside plant tissues (endophytically), e.g. the larvae of buprestids, longhorn beetles, weevils, etc. The larvae of all beetles generally have well-developed chewing mouthparts.

In some parasitic beetle larvae we come across what is known as polymetaboly. The individual larval instars of these species exhibit marked morphological differences. The first instar moves about, lives freely, and actively seeks out its host. The ensuing instars are more or less parasitic, move about very little and have reduced limbs. This type of development is encountered in some ground beetles (of the genera *Brachinus, Aptinus,* and *Lebia,*) rove beetles (the subfamily Aleocharinae), and beetles of the family Rhipiphoridae. Closely linked with this phenomenon is the one known as hypermetamorphosis, during which there is another quiescent stage, besides the pupa, in the developmental cycle. It is a very complex development encountered, for example, in the case of blister beetles (Meloidae).

The pupa is a stage of outward inactivity but with great changes inside, during which the larval organs undergo a complex transformation into the organs of the adult beetle (imaginal organs). During this transformation there is a complete dissolution of the tissues followed by the growth of new tissue and the formation of the internal organs of the future adult insect from imaginal discs. Only during the pupal stage is it possible to see the formation of the external imaginal organs, e.g. wings and genitalia. There are two types of pupae: exarate and obtect. Both types are to be found amongst beetles. The exarate

Heads of beetles: a, prognathous (Staphylinidae); b, opisthognathous (Mordellidae); c, hypognathous (Buprestidae).

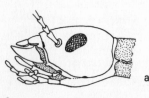
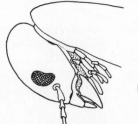
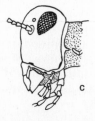

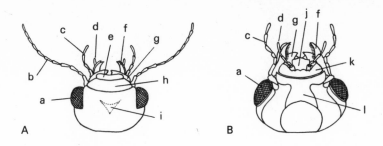

Diagram of the chewing mouthparts of a beetle: A, dorsal view; B, ventral view:
a, eye; b, antenna; c, maxillary palp; d, labial palp; e, labrum; f, maxilla;
g, mandible; h, clypeus, i, front; j, labium; k, praementum; l, gula.

pupa has the body appendages (wings, legs, antennae) free and is non-sclerotized and coloured white or creamy-white. It is generally enclosed in a pupal cell or cocoon and is common to the great majority of beetles. The obtect pupa, on the other hand, has all the body appendages firmly fixed to the body, its cuticle is sclerotized and generally also strongly pigmented. This 'mummy-like' pupa is less common amongst beetles, occurring, for example, in the Staphylinidae and Coccinellidae families and in some members of the Chrysomelidae.

The body of beetles consists of the head, thorax and abdomen.

The head of beetles may be prolonged in line with the body's longitudinal axis with the mouthparts pointing forward (prognathous). It may be bent downward at right angles to the body's axis (hypognathous), or it may be bent downward and pointing toward the hind end (opistognathous). The mouthparts are always adapted for chewing, except in the subfamily Nemognathinae of the family Meloidae, whose members have the mouthparts adapted for sucking. Chewing mouthparts are made up of the upper lip or labrum, which is generally movably attached to the anterior portion of the head capsule called the clypeus. Below the labrum are the mandibles, or upper pair of jaws. Below these are the maxillae, or second pair of jaws, and below the maxillae there is the lower lip or labium. The labrum is generally sclerotized above and membranous beneath with a field of sensory bristles (epipharynx). The mandibles are always strongly sclerotized, curved to sickle-shaped, in the males of some species strikingly prolonged (e.g. the Stag Beetle). In some beetles with extra-oral digestion (glow-worms) there is a narrow duct in the mandibles through which digestive juices are injected into the beetle's prey. The maxillae are composed of two basal segments (cardo and stipes) which bear two outgrowths (galea and lacinia) and as a rule maxillary palps — four-segmented appendages. The labium is composed of two basic segments (praementum and gula) bearing paired outgrowths known

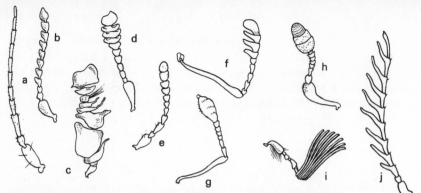

Types of beetle antennae: a, filiform; b, serrate; c, greatly modified (*Cerocoma*);
d, capitate; e, moniliform; f, geniculate-lamellate; g, geniculate-clavate;
h, geniculate-capitate; i, lamellate; j, pectinate.

as the glossae and paraglossae and in most beetles also labial palps,
which are made up of three segments. Inside the mouth cavity, between the labium and maxillae, there is usually a membranous fold
(hypopharynx) bearing countless various hairs and papillae that serve
as organs of taste.

The most striking appendages on the head are the movable antennae, attached by means of a hinged joint. The antennae of beetles are
usually composed of eleven segments, but in some species they may
be greatly reduced due to the insects' parasitic way of life (the Clavigeridae and Paussidae families). Some species have twelve-jointed
antennae (e.g. the males of certain longhorn beetles of the genera
Molorchus, Agapanthia and *Prionus*), or else the number of segments
may be secondarily increased to as many as 40 (male longhorn beetles
of the genus *Polyarthron*). The antennae of beetles vary greatly in
shape — ranging from the simple setaceous antennae of the ground
beetles, through serrate, pectinate, capitate, and variously bent antennae to the strange dish-like appendages of myrmecophilous beetles
and beetles that live in the company of termites. Antennae serve primarily as organs of touch and smell, but may also serve as organs
capable of perceiving electromagnetic waves, humidity, infra-red
radiation and apparently other physical phenomena as well.

The eyes of beetles are generally well developed. They are of the
compound type and composed of numbers of tiny sections known as
ommatidia. Each ommatidium has a separate lens and receptor and
forms an image of a certain section of space, the images from the various ommatidia then being combined in the brain to form a mosaic
image of the complete field of view. The compound eyes of beetles
may be large and protruding (e.g. in the Cicindelidae), oval, kidney-
shaped or elliptical, occasionally small, spherical and in rare in-

10

stances totally reduced. Such reduced eyes are to be found in species of ground beetles that live in caves or permanently underground, in members of the Clavigeridae family that live in ant nests, and in all species of the Bathyscidae family. Sometimes the eye is divided into two parts either by the base of the antennae or by various bars (whirligig beetles, some longhorn beetles and stag-beetles).

Simple eyes (ocelli) are only rarely found in beetles, and, where they do occur, it is always together with a pair of compound eyes; the ocelli are located between the compound eyes — e.g. in some dermestids.

The thorax of beetles consists of the prothorax, mesothorax and metathorax. The most prominent feature is the pronotum — the large, generally flat or slightly convex dorsal part of the prothorax which varies greatly in sculpture. The only visible part of the mesothorax is the scutellum, which is generally semicircular, pentagonal or triangular, and is wedged in between the bases of the elytra. In rare instances the scutellum cannot be seen because it is hidden either by the elytra or by the hind edge of the pronotum. The metathorax cannot be seen from above.

All three thoracic segments bear paired appendages: each segment bears one pair of legs and the mesothorax and metathorax each bear a pair of wings. The first pair of wings are attached to the mesothorax, and are the hard, strongly sclerotized elytra, which generally cover the entire abdomen while the hind, membranous wings are attached to the metathorax. In some instances the elytra are shorter than the body and do not cover the abdomen. In such cases the membranous second pair of wings are either folded beneath the abbreviated elytra, e.g. in the majority of rove beetles, or extend from beneath the abbreviated elytra and cover the abdomen e.g. in certain longhorn beetles (*Molorchus, Glaphyra, Necydalis*), in species of the genus *Rhipidius* and in certain blister beetles (*Sitaris*).

The second pair of wings are membranous with more or less developed venation and serve for flying. Frequently, however, these hind wings are reduced to mere scale-like or non-functional structures. Such a reduction of the hind wings may be observed, for example, in some ground beetles, weevils, blister beetles of the genus *Meloe,*

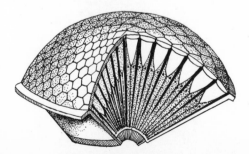

Schematic section through the compound eye of a beetle.

11

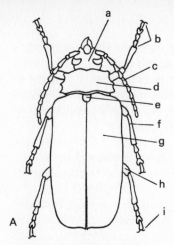

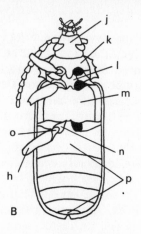

Diagram of a beetle body: A, dorsal view; B, ventral view: a, head; b, tarsus; c, antenna; d, pronotum; e, scutellum; f, tibia; g, elytra; h, femur; i, claws; j, gula; k, prothorax; l, mesothorax; m, metathorax; n, coxa; o, trochanter; p, abdominal segments.

longhorn beetles of the genus *Dorcadion,* and many others. The hind wings of members of the family Ptiliidae are modified into fine, feather-like structures. Some beetles do not possess even rudimentary elytra or wings. Such a general, naturally secondary apterous (wingless) condition may be found in females of the Lampyridae and Drilidae families.

Most beetles have legs adapted for walking. In species that run rapidly, e.g. Cicindelidae, the legs are extremely thin and long — basically this is the simplest modification of this type of leg. Some members of the Scarabeidae and Tenebrionidae families have legs adapted for burrowing, beetles of the family Alticidae, some weevils (genus *Orchestes*) and some species of the family Serropalpidae have jumping legs, while legs adapted for swimming may be found in the

Beetle legs adapted for: a, running; b, swimming; c, burrowing; d, jumping; e, adhesion; f, paddling.

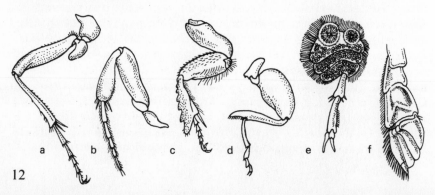

Dytiscidae, Haliplidae and Gyrinidae, and in some Hydrophilidae.

The leg of a beetle (and of insects in general) consists of the coxa, trochanter, femur, tibia and tarsus, which is composed of segments that may be variously modified. The last joint is fitted with two claws (very occasionally only one). The claws may be simply curved, sickle-shaped or hooked, and may be furnished with one or a great number of teeth. Frequently the tarsal joints have organs of adhesion on the underside (plates, cushions, adhesive pads) that serve to keep a firm hold on the substrate or to grip the female during copulation.

The abdomen consists of eleven segments in the embryonic stage but in the adult beetle the number of segments is reduced. In the females of some species the terminal segments are modified into a retractable ovipositor with the aid of which the female deposits eggs in cracks in the ground, in bark, in wood, or directly inside plant tissue. Adult beetles do not have any visible abdominal appendages.

The terminal abdominal segments contain the genitalia. In males it is the ninth abdominal segment that bears the external organ of copulation known as the penis or aedeagus. The female genitalia are formed by the eighth and ninth abdominal segment.

FOOD

Beetles may be carnivorous, phytophagous or omnivorous. In many cases there is a marked difference between the diet of the larva and that of the adult beetle. There are even instances where the larva is carnivorous and the adult beetle phytophagous, e.g. some species of click-beetles (Elateridae) and blister-beetles (Meloidae). In some instances the adult beetle does not feed at all (e.g. members of the families Lampyridae, Drilidae, Rhipiphoridae). There are great differences between the diet of the larva and the imago even amongst phytophagous beetles. In a great number of species the larvae feed on wood (they are xylophagous) whereas the adult beetles feed on flowers or plant pollen (they are anthophagous or polinophagous). This is quite common, for example, in members of the families Alleculidae, Mordellidae, Oedemeridae, Cerambycidae and Buprestidae.

There are many different types of carnivorous beetles, specialized in different ways. First and foremost there are the predators that hunt live food, chiefly various insects and their larvae. These include the Cicindelidae, most ground beetles, Dytiscidae, Gyrinidae, Haliplidae and the larvae of some click-beetles. Insects and their larvae are not the only food predacious beetles feed on. The larvae as well as adults of large species of diving beetles of the genus *Dytiscus* may add variety to their diet by eating small fish, tadpoles and even adult frogs and water-newts. Some large species of desert ground beetles (e. g. members of the genera *Scarites* and *Anthia*) occasionally capture even a smaller lizard or gecko. Predacious beetles include species that specialize in feeding on slugs and snails. Examples are the large ground beetles of the genera *Carabus* and *Procerus* and the larvae of glow-worms.

There are parasitic species that develop in the nests of social insects (ants, termites, wasps, etc.) and that feed on the larvae or pupae of these insects. They include numerous species of rove-beetles (Staphylinidae), blister beetles (Meloidae), Rhipiphoridae and some members of the families Thorictidae, Histeridae as well as Cleridae. A separate group of food specialists amongst carnivorous beetles are the aphidophagous species, in other words species that feed on aphids. These include numerous ladybirds, whose larvae as well as adult forms actively hunt aphids and scale-insects.

Necrophagous species, i.e. those that feed on decaying animal matter, chiefly vertebrate carrion, also belong to the group of carnivorous beetles. They act as scavengers and thus play an important role in disposing of waste matter and making it reavailable. Best known are the carrion beetles, but some members of the families Catopidae and Scarabaeidae likewise belong to this group.

The last group of carnivorous beetles are the true parasites of vertebrates. In Europe there are only three species of beetles, all members of the family Leptinidae, that are parasites on mammals. One lives in the furry coat of rodents and insectivores, another in the fur of beavers and the third in the fur of the Russian Desman (*Desmana moschata*).

Another large group are the phytophagous beetles. These comprise all the species that feed on plant tissues (living, dying or decayed) or plant products. Species that feed on plant tissues may be divided roughly into those that feed from within plant tissues (endophagous beetles) and those that feed on the plant from the outside (exophagous beetles). They may further be divided into those that feed on non-woody plant tissues and those that feed on wood or bark (xylophagous beetles). Mycetophagous species that feed on the mycelium or fruit-bodies of fungi form a separate group of phytophagous beetles. There are many such species and even entire families that specialize in this mode of obtaining food, namely the Mycetophagidae, Endomychidae, Erotylidae, Lathridiidae, Cryptophagidae, Ptiliidae, Cisidae, Liodidae, and many more. Some species develop inside fruits (Byturidae) or in seeds (Bruchidae, certain Curculionidae). The fermenting sap of bruised trees serves as food for a great many bee-

14

tles, for instance members of the family Nosodendridae. The adult beetles of some species feed on pollen grains. Such species are called polinophagous and include, for example, numerous Nitidulidae, Buprestidae and Cerambycidae. Interesting and very restricted is the food specialization of members of the family Phalacridae. The larvae (and apparently also the adult beetles) feed on rusts and smuts, chiefly those of grasses.

An unusual type of food specialization is that of coprophagous beetles, which may be classed as phytophagous because they feed on plant remnants in the dung of herbivores. They comprise a vast number of beetles, chiefly members of the Scarabaeidae and Hydrophilidae families.

The last group are the omnivorous beetles. These include species that feed mostly on various organic, both plant and animal, remnants, which as a rule are already partly decayed. Many such species are to be found in the family Tenebrionidae as well as in the Scarabaeidae, Histeridae, Cryptophagidae and Ptinidae families.

With their biting mouthparts beetles first of all chew or suck up their food. Paired salivary glands open into the mouth cavity, and their secretion serves as the first step in the digesting of the food. From there the food passes through the oesophagus to the crop and thence to the proventriculus, whose digestive surface is enlarged by numerous blind vessels varying in length and number and secreting digestive juices. The partially digested food passes on through the middle gut, into which the excretory organs (Malpighian tubes) open, and through the hind gut to the rectum, which ends in the anus or posterior opening of the alimentary canal in the last abdominal segment. In many species there are rectal papillae in the region of the rectum that serve to reabsorb water, thereby helping the body conserve its water supply (these are particularly well developed in desert species).

An unusual form of digestion, known as extra-oral digestion, is found in the larvae of beetles of the Dytiscidae, Haliplidae, Gyrinidae, and Lampyridae families. The digestive juices of the anterior part of the alimentary canal are injected by the larva into its prey via a narrow duct that passes through its sickle-shaped mandibles. The partially digested (liquefied) contents of its prey are then sucked up through this mandibular duct.

RESPIRATION

Beetles respire with the aid of internal air-conveying tubules called tracheae, which branch into increasingly smaller tubules that finally terminate in the finest tubules called tracheoles. Tracheoles entwine all important organs and muscles and extend even into the wings via the veins. On the outside of the body the tracheae terminate in small apertures called spiracles, located along each side of the thorax and abdomen. In some species (especially large ones) it is possible to observe the physical act of breathing, so-called pumping, which takes place mainly prior to flying up into the air.

Beetles are adapted in various ways to different habitats and this also includes adaptations in the manner of obtaining their supply of oxygen. The larvae of aquatic beetles (Dytiscidae, Haliplidae, Gyrinidae, Psephenidae and some species of the family Hydrophilidae) have palmate gills on either side of the abdominal segments, with the aid of which they absorb the oxygen in the water, or else obtain oxygen from the atmosphere by means of the terminal pair of abdominal spiracles which they thrust above the water's surface. Adult beetles that live in water carry a supply of air beneath their elytra which they pump there from the atmosphere via the tip of the abdomen or the antennae which they thrust above the water's surface.

Beetles of the family Elmidae have adopted a different technique. They carry air trapped between the short, dense, impermeable hairs which clothe the underside of their body. The larvae of certain leaf beetles of the genera *Plateumaris* and *Donacia,* which live on aquatic plants, tap the plant's air supply by means of a hook-like structure at the tip of their abdomen taking the required oxygen directly from the plant tissues. Pupae of the small family Psephenidae possess so-called spiracular gills. These are long protrusions of the inner wall of the spiracles by means of which the pupa, whose development takes place in water, obtains oxygen from the water.

REPRODUCTION

Most beetle species have separate males and females. Only in some species of the genus *Otiorrhynchus* are males very rare or absent altogether. Here females produce female offspring without their eggs being fertilized by males; this form of reproduction is known as parthenogenesis. This is also found in a number of beetle species of the little known tropical family Micromalthidae.

Males and females locate each other by various scent signals, so-called sex pheromones, which can be detected by individuals of the opposite sex from a considerable distance. In some instances the two sexes locate each other by means of visual signals, e.g. in the Phengodidae and Lampyridae families and in certain tropical beetles of the genus *Pyrophorus* and several other related genera. Only rarely do males and females locate one another by means of sound signals — e.g. the tapping of Anobiidae, the stridulation of certain longhorn beetles. During copulation sperm cells are transferred in the form of large masses of spermatozoa called spermatophores that may be enclosed in various kinds of protein envelopes. Copulation is sometimes preceded by so-called epigamous behaviour, e.g. various posturing by the male or duels between males, which, however, never end in the death of the weaker individual but merely in his retreat.

Almost all beetle species are oviparous and the development of the embryo takes place outside the female's body. The eggs are generally deposited in places where the newly emerged larva is immediately provided with food (on various plant parts in the case of phytophagous species, on decaying plant or animal remains in the case of saprophagous species, in dung in the case of coprophagous species, and in places rich in prey in the case of predacious species).

Viviparity (producing living young) is uncommon in beetles and occurs only in one species of leaf beetle — *Chrysolina variana*. The developing eggs are retained inside the body of the female and obtain nourishment from the follicular epithelium inside the ovary. The female then 'gives birth' to the larva in the emergent stage.

After the eggs have been laid most female beetles devote no more attention to the care of their brood although some show parental care. The simplest type of parental care is exhibited by the ground beetles of the genus *Molops,* where the female watches over the eggs until the larvae emerge. More complex is the care exhibited by tropical beetles of the family Passalidae, where the females, besides caring for the eggs, also watch over the larvae until they pupate. The most sophisticated parental care is that of the coprophagous beetles of the family Scarabaeidae. The female (sometimes with the aid of the male) often builds a relatively complicated burrow in the ground which she provisions with dung into which the eggs are deposited. She does not abandon the nest until the larvae have pupated. Often she does not leave the nest at all but dies there.

LOCOMOTION

Terrestrial beetles have two basic forms of locomotion: walking and flying. For the purpose of walking or its modifications (running, jumping) beetles have three pairs of legs attached by a hinged joint to the thorax. Used for flying is the second, membranous pair of wings, generally concealed beneath the wing-cases or elytra when the beetle is at rest. In a great many species, however, the wings have degenerated and the insects are wingless and incapable of flight.

When walking, whether slowly or rapidly (running), the beetle always touches the substrate simultaneously with three legs (so-called tripod theory of locomotion). Rapid runners, in particular Cicindelidae and Carabidae, are capable of moving at unbelievable speed. Most Cicindelidae are furthermore good fliers and capable of becoming airborne in a flash, which makes it practically impossible to catch them. Some desert species, especially the Tenebrionidae, have developed an unusual slow, almost hesitant manner of walking on their long, practically erect legs so that the underside of the body never comes in contact with the burning hot sand, not even when the beetle is motionless (this prevents overheating of the organism and excessive loss of water).

Aquatic beetles have the legs modified into more or less perfect organs adapted for swimming, paddling or steering, which on dry land would be a very clumsy means of locomotion. Such legs are to be found chiefly in the Dytiscidae, Haliplidae and Gyrinidae families and in some Hydrophilidae.

In flight the wings perform many complex movements both lengthwise and crosswise. The tip of the wing generally describes a curve resembling the figure eight on its side instead of upright. When flying most beetles have both elytra uptilted at an angle. There are naturally many exceptions when the elytra cover the abdomen even during flight. Chafers of the subfamily Cetoniinae fly in this manner, for instance, as do some buprestids of the subfamily Acmaeoderinae.

Beetles that are secondarily wingless and are therefore unable to fly include members of the Carabidae, Scarabaeidae, Byrrhidae, Nosodendridae, Elateridae, Thorictidae, Tenebrionidae, Meloidae, Cerambycidae, Chrysomelidae, Curculionidae and many other families. Wingless, flightless species are even to be found in the Cicindelidae and Buprestidae families, whose members are among the fastest-flying beetles of all. The Lampyridae, Drilidae and Cebrionidae families include species in which the males fly and the females are incapable of flight, and the same is true of certain longhorn beetles of the subfamilies Prioninae and Vesperinae. In the smallest known beetles (Ptilidae) the membranous wings have been modified into feather-like structures fringed with long hairs that are not used for strong flight but more to enable the beetle to be borne by air currents.

SPECIAL ADAPTATIONS

Beetles inhabit many diverse environments and during the course of evolution have developed many important adaptations that help them survive in widely varied conditions.

18

Many morphological as well as physiological adaptations have been developed by aquatic beetles. These include first and foremost legs adapted for swimming and paddling and various adaptations for breathing underwater, as well as physiological adaptations to life in brackish and often strongly salt water. Life in rapidly flowing mountain streams requires that the beetle and its larva be capable of remaining in a suitable spot and not be carried off by the current to less suitable habitats in the lower reaches of the stream. Such species are generally equipped with strong, hooked claws (Dryopidae).

The opposite of life in water is life in extremely dry conditions, mainly in deserts, but also, for example, in stores of foodstuffs and grain. Species that inhabit such stores are discussed in the section on the economic importance of beetles. Desert beetles must be adapted primarily to dry conditions, but furthermore also to heat and extreme variations between daytime and night-time temperature. The simplest solution is to be active by night, when the temperature drops and atmospheric humidity rises. Some species of Tenebrionidae are even able to condense atmospheric moisture into droplets of water on their body in the cooler hours of early morning. Simultaneously they adopt a characteristic posture with hind legs erect and head down. This position causes the small droplets of water that have condensed on the smooth surface of the body to flow forward until they reach the mouth. Species that wait out the day's heat buried deep in the sand have legs adapted for burrowing. Other species of desert beetles (once again mostly Tenebrionidae) protect their bodies from becoming overheated and losing an excessive amount of water by means of various waxy coatings on the elytra, generally coloured white, or by means of an air cushion beneath the markedly convex elytra which look as if they were inflated.

Some beetles live more or less permanently in the ground, which likewise has given rise to many special adaptations. These beetles are generally small, and either stout with the front pair of legs adapted for burrowing if they live in loose matter (e.g. certain Tenebrionidae) or slender with longer legs and antennae if they live in cracks in the ground or under stones (e.g. certain ground beetles). Living underground has generally resulted in the reduction of the eyes, loss of pigmentation and a greater number and lengthening of various sensory hairs.

Some beetles have become adapted to life in ants' and termites' nests. This way of life has in some instances been adopted by entire families (Paussidae, Clavigeridae, Thorictidae, Meriophysidae), whereas in others only by certain genera of some families (Staphylinidae, Histeridae, Pselaphidae, Colydiidae, Cucujidae, Scarabaeidae, etc.).

Most of the species found in ants' nests are totally dependent on the ants and unable to survive elsewhere. Many of these species are 'pampered' beetles (symphyls) so dependent on the care of the ants or termites that they can no longer live without them.

The beetles produce secretions which attract the ants; they may even vibrate their antennae to stimulate the ants. The ants lick the secretions and in return feed the beetles. Sometimes this relationship goes so far that the ants are afflicted by a kind of drug addiction, cease caring properly for their offspring and devote their attention mostly to these myrmecophilous beetles. The larvae of these beetles are generally predacious and feed on the larvae of the ants.

Beetles also include among their number species that look like a mound of earth or a pebble, that resemble a dry twig, leaf, piece of bark or chip of wood, or even bird faeces. Other beetles mimic poisonous or otherwise dangerous insects. The most striking examples are to be found amongst the longhorn beetles, which mimic a wasp or a hornet, not only in the coloration and shape of the body, but in their movement as well, and also amongst the Buprestidae, Chrysomelidae and Scarabaeidae. Poisonous beetles are likewise imitated by other, entirely harmless species. A few species of beetles are poisonous and these are mostly members of Meloidae and Lycidae. The active constituent of their poison, which is present in the haemolymph, is the alkaloid cantharidin. These species, which are sometimes extremely poisonous, are generally brightly coloured. The best known example is the blister beetle *Lytta vesicatoria,* which was even used as a medicine or as an aphrodisiac in medieval days. In recent years similar substances have been discovered in some Buprestidae.

DISTRIBUTION

Apart from the region of permanent ice and snow on the world's highest mountain peaks or North and South Poles, beetles are to be found everywhere. Naturally different species, genera and often families are to be found in Europe, Africa, the Americas and Australia because the early geological history and evolution of the climate differed in each of these continents. Zoogeographers therefore divide the world into six basic zoogeographical regions: the Palaearctic, Nearctic, Ethiopian (or Afrotropical), Oriental (Indo-Malayan), Neotropical, and Australasian. The evolution of the Palaearctic and Nearctic regions, both of which are located in the temperate zone of the northern hemisphere, took place under similar conditions and the two regions have many characteristics in common. For this reason they can be considered as a single region called the Holarctic.

Some of the most primitive, and geologically oldest beetles, as with many animals and plants, are found in the Australasian region, in the Madagascar subregion of the Ethiopian region, and in the southern part of the Neotropical region. This is due primarily to the fact that these continents were all linked in a supercontinent and the last connections were mostly via the southern continent.

In historic times, of course, the distribution of many animal species, and hence also beetles, has been affected by man. The development of transport and the spread of cultivated plants brought with them also marked changes in the area of distribution of many species of beetles. One example is the Colorado Beetle (*Leptinotarsa decemlineata*), which originally inhabited. only the western United States and is now found in all parts of the world where potatoes are grown. The same is true of a great many small species (mostly pests of stored foodstuffs) of the Cucujidae, Trogossitidae and Bostrychidae families which nowadays have a worldwide distribution thanks to the storing of foodstuffs in air-conditioned warehouses and stores. The spread of some beetle species far beyond the borders of their natural area of distribution was sometimes brought about by man as a means of biological control. Thus, for example, many species of coprophagous beetles of the family Scarabaeidae were introduced from Africa to similar climatic conditions in Australia to help eradicate the enormous quantities of dung produced by imported herbivores (sheep and cows). Another such example is *Sphenoptera jugoslavica,* whose larvae live inside the roots of the cornflower *Centaurea diffusa* in southern Europe. This beetle was recently introduced with great success into the USA, where it is helping eradicate weeds in cornfields. It is literally a textbook example of the effective biological control of field weeds.

ECONOMIC IMPORTANCE OF BEETLES

The beetles' great diversity of species and ecology renders it only natural that some have come in conflict with man. Let us first take a look at their effect on our health. Beetles are not known to be direct parasites on man but some 500 species (mainly coprophagous and necrophagous beetles) serve as intermediate hosts for tapeworms, roundworms and other endoparasites of veterinary importance.

Leaving aside the relatively negligible damage caused by the larvae and adult forms of predacious diving beetles on the fry in fish-breeding ponds, the most important pests are the phytophagous and xylophagous species. Common pests in agriculture are Colorado Beetles and Pollen Beetles (*Meligethes aeneus*). The number of important field pests is of course much greater: they include various other Chrysomelidae, Bruchidae, Curculionidae, the larvae of many species of Elateridae as well as the larvae and adult beetles of various species of Scarabaeidae. The number of those that are pests of woodland and forest is even greater. They include species that feed on leaves and needles (cockchafers, leaf-beetles, weevils), roots (click-beetles, weevils), fruits and cones (Byturidae, weevils), and above all xylophagous species that either damage wood intended for furniture (technical pests) or damage living trees (primary pests). Heading the list of primary pests are the bark beetles (Scolytidae), the most notorious being *Ips typographus,* which has already caused much damage from which forests in parts of Europe have scarcely recovered. The group of primary pests also includes many species of longhorn beetles, buprestids and scolytids, the latter being responsible for the spread of Dutch Elm disease. Technical pests that feed on wood likewise include many longhorn beetles and buprestids, as well as members of the Lymexylonidae and Bostrychidae families.

Household and warehouse pests comprise another group which includes members of many families and in some cases cosmopolitan species. Most notorious are certain Tenebrionidae such as *Tenebrio molitor* and *Tribolium destructor,* which together with several species of anobiids (e.g. *Stegobium paniceum*) and cucujids (*Oryzaephilus surinamensis,* genus *Laemophloeus*) are among the most feared pests of stored foodstuffs. Pests of stored cereals include also the weevil *Calandra granaria* and a member of the Trogossitidae family — *Tenebrioides mauritanicus.*

Households are invaded by other beetle species that are troublesome pests. Heading the list are the carpet beetles (Dermestidae), some of which cause damage to leather and fabrics (genera *Dermestes* and *Attagenus*), foodstuffs (*Trogoderma granarium*), and insect collections, stuffed animals, etc. (*Anthrenus museorum*). The anobiids likewise include many such pests. As well as the aforementioned species *Stegobium paniceum* it is first and foremost *Anobium punctatum,* or woodworm, which may develop in large numbers in old timber and furniture. Relatively rare in the household is the species *Lasioderma serricorne* which specializes in feeding on tobacco products.

Beetles that are of economic importance, however, include not only pests but also a vast number of very beneficial species. Ground beetles, apart from a few exceptions (genus *Zabrus*), are extremely useful because they are predacious and feed on many other very harmful insect pests. The same is true of the Cicindelidae, Staphylinidae, and the larvae of Histeridae. Another group of ecological importance are the saprophagous beetles that feed on carrion (Silphidae, Catopidae) and coprophagous beetles (Scarabaeidae) that feed on dung.

Definitely beneficial are most species of ladybird that feed on aphids. Many members of this family have been used with success in the biological control of aphids and mealybugs. Beetles are very important as pollinators. These include practically all beetles that regularly rest on flowers.

THE STUDY, REARING AND BREEDING, PHOTO-GRAPHING AND CONSERVATION OF BEETLES

The breeding of beetles and rearing of their developmental stages should go hand in hand with the study of these insects; it generally does not require any costly equipment and is an area in which the amateur can really contribute useful information. If, for example, you wish to observe the behaviour of aquatic beetles all you need is an ordinary aquarium. The larvae of these species are all predacious and even feeding them presents no special problems. Usually small aquatic insects, earthworms, or even just small bits of meat will suffice. Rearing and observing predacious terrestrial beetles is also quite simple. All that is required is a sufficiently deep container with an adequately thick substrate layer (soil, sand, peat) and a hiding place such as a piece of bark or stone. Such species are generally fed the larvae of other insects, mainly mealworms, or small slugs. Great care must naturally be taken to keep the substrate adequately moist — it must never become too dry and should never be too damp. Necrophagous and coprophagous beetles are reared in the same way. These, of course, require a thick substrate for building their nests, which are often complex and deep constructions, as well as natural food.

Rearing phytophagous and xylophagous beetles is far more complicated. Most larvae of phytophagous beetles require a constant supply of fresh food which often presents difficulties. And in the case of xylophagous species, the adult beetles of some often feed on an entirely different plant from that on which the larvae develop. Without such food the beetles frequently will not even mate. Xylophagous beetles, e.g. buprestids or longhorn beetles, are generally reared by placing a female already fertilized in the wild in a container with the woody material the larva feeds on and leaving her to deposit the eggs there. A surer method is to transfer to the container an entire piece of a branch that has been infested by the species which is to be reared. Here, once again, the problem is keeping the substrate adequately moist. Some species develop in dead wood, others in dying or even living wood. In the last instance rearing adult beetles from the larvae poses great problems.

23

Rearing and observing species whose larvae develop in the decayed, crumbling wood of old trees (cetoniids, stag beetles) is relatively easy. All they need is a sufficiently large container with rotting, crumbling wood, which, of course, must be kept as moist as the larvae are accustomed to in the wild. Their diet should be supplemented with pieces of sweet fruit.

Beetles are raised not merely for study purposes. Many people keep beetles for their beauty and interesting behaviour, in the same way as others keep aquarium fish. Most beetles have a relatively short life span as adults. Some, of course, may live even several years and it is the latter that are the most rewarding subjects for keeping in an insectarium and for observation. They include chiefly large Tenebrionidae of the genera *Blaps, Pimelia, Akis* and others. These are very undemanding species, some measuring even several centimetres in length, that need no more than a sandy or partly stony substrate in an insectarium, very occasional moistening, and any kind of organic matter as food. Large ground beetles of the genus *Carabus,* which have a life-span of up to three years as adults, may be reared in the same manner.

Those who rear beetles and observe their habits will find taking photographs of them rewarding. With the high quality of present-day cameras and films even the amateur can take a good and interesting picture of a beetle. Beetles should always be photographed in their natural habitat unless the pictures are intended to be special shots of various details or organs. In other words they should be photographed in their natural environment in the wild or in an insectarium arranged to resemble as much as possible the natural habitat of the photographed species. Because beetles are usually small it is necessary to employ a close-up (macro) lens or extension rings or bellows to extend the focal length. Even when taking pictures in the wild there may not be sufficient light and thus it is necessary to use an electronic flash, best of all a ring-flash or two opposite flashes. When taking pictures of a fast-moving species its activity can be reduced briefly by cooling the beetle in the refrigerator or else by applying a non-toxic anaesthetic. However, these actions may leave the beetle in a less life-like position.

The conservation of beetles is inseparably linked with the protection of the environment. Conservation of individual rare or endangered species is naturally of importance as well. It is not necessary to kill dozens of specimens of a single species for the purpose of making a collection. It is necessary to be prudent in the use of various traps, with or without bait — you should avoid damaging the environment. The development of a great many beetles takes place in old trees and it is these very trees, old hollow specimens, that are often selectively removed from forests though they are the very ones that should be protected for the benefit of the beetles. In this manner it is possible to exterminate completely, for example, certain species of click-beetles (Elateridae), cetoniids and longhorn beetles. Widespread use of chemicals altering the soil or mechanical disturbance has already caused the disappearance of various species of ground beetles, rove beetles, weevils, and leaf-beetles. Pollution of ponds and streams will destroy the habitat of water beetles.

The greatest danger not only for beetles but for the whole environment, however, is destruction of the environment whether by chemical substances used in forestry and agriculture or emitted by industrial plants into the atmosphere or into water. When a chemical is sprayed to control pests, all other insect species in the area will be destroyed, including those which are natural predators of many pests. Unscrupulously unloaded waste water by factories and the excessive use of detergents can destroy all life even in large rivers and lakes. The vast quantities of gasses constantly spewed by factories into the atmosphere can, in the form of fall-out and acid rain, destroy whole forests. Herein lies the greatest threat to man's environment and hence also to beetles. Beetles, just as many other groups of insects, are sometimes bound to quite definite, small and specific biotopes, often so isolated from one another that a whole population may be destroyed by the effect of a heedless act.

THE CLASSIFICATION OF BEETLES

The order Coleoptera is divided here into four suborders: Adephaga, Archostemata, Myxophaga and Polyphaga. At the present time the order has about 175 families, but the systematic position of some species and genera is disputed and the total number of families varies according to the expert consulted. Disagreement in the systematic position of some Coleoptera has led to differences in classification. The classification used here follows Imms (1957) and Crowson (1981).

The suborder Adephaga comprises carnivorous beetles with legs generally adapted for rapid running. In this book they are to be found on p. 28—53. Included here are the following families: Rhysodidae, Carabidae, Trachypachydae, Haliplidae, Amphizoidae, Hygrobiidae, Noteridae, Dytiscidae and Gyrinidae.

The suborder Archostemata comprises a group of beetle families with very primitive wing venation and elytra of complex structure. Only a single species is illustrated in this book, on p. 53; the great majority of species are found only in the tropics. The families included in this suborder are as follows: Ommadidae, Tetraphaleridae, Cupedidae, and Micromalthidae.

The suborder Myxophaga comprises extremely small, inconspicuous and economically unimportant species with reduced wing venation and concealed way of life. It comprises only 4 families, not included in the pictorial section, namely: Lepiceridae, Torridincolidae, Hydroscaphidae, and Sphaeriidae.

The suborder Polyphaga comprises the vast majority of beetles varying widely in body structure and divided into a great number of families (pictorial section pp. 54—219) as follows: Hydraenidae, Sprecheidae, Hydrochidae, Georyssidae, Hydrophilidae, Sphaeritidae, Synteliidae, Histeridae, Ptiliidae, Empelidae, Anisotomidae, Catopidae, Leptinidae, Scydmaenidae, Silphidae, Micropeplidae, Dasyceridae, Staphylinidae, Pselaphidae, Clambidae, Eucinetidae, Helodidae, Dascillidae, Karumiidae, Rhipiceridae, Lucanidae, Trogidae, Acanthoceridae, Passalidae, Pleocomidae, Geotrupidae, Ochodaeidae, Hybosoridae, Glaphyridae, Scarabaeidae, Byrrhidae, Eulichadidae, Ptilodactylidae, Chelonariidae, Psephenidae, Elmidae, Lutrochidae, Dryopidae, Limnichidae, Heteroceridae, Buprestidae, Artematopidae, Callirhipidae, Brachypsectridae, Cebrionidae, Elateridae, Throscidae, Eucnemidae, Cneoglossidae, Plastoceridae, Homalisidae, Lycidae, Drilidae, Phengodidae, Telegeusidae, Lampyridae, Omethidae, Cantharidae, Derodontidae, Nosondendridae, Dermestidae, Thorictidae, Jakobsoniidae, Bostrychidae, Anobiidae, Phloiophilidae, Peltidae, Lophocateridae, Trogossitidae, Chaetosomatidae, Acanthocnemidae, Cleridae, Phycosecidae, Melyridae, Lymexylidae, Stylopidae, Nitidulidae, Rhizophagidae, Boganiidae, Phalacridae, Protocucujidae, Sphindidae, Hobartiidae, Cucujidae, Passandridae, Phloeostichidae, Silvanidae, Cavognathidae, Cryptophagidae, Helotidae, Byturidae, Biphyllidae, Lamingtoniidae, Languridae, Erotylidae, Cryptophilidae, Cerylonidae, Corylophidae, Sphaerosomatidae, Endomychidae, Coccinellidae, Discolomidae, Merophysiidae, Lathridiidae, Merycidae, Colydiidae, Prostomidae, Mycetophagidae, Cisidae, Petrogeniidae, Tetratomidae, Melandryidae, Mordellidae, Rhipiphoridae, Synchroidae, Cephaloidae, Oedemeridae, Pythidae, Pyrochroidae, Anthicidae, Aderidae, Meloidae, Scraptiidae, Cononotidae, Othniidae, Salpingidae, Inopeplidae, Mycteridae, Monotommidae, Zopheridae, Lagriidae, Tenebrionidae, Disteniidae, Cerambycidae, Megalopodidae, Bruchidae, Chrysomelidae, Nemonychidae, Anthribidae, Belidae, Oxycorynidae, Aglycyderidae, Attelabidae, Apionidae, Brenthidae, Curculionidae, Scolytidae, Platypodidae.

26

COLOUR PLATES

Wood Tiger Beetle
Cicindela silvatica LINNÉ, 1758   Carabidae

The Wood Tiger Beetle, distributed throughout Europe, is the largest European representative of the subfamily Cicindelinae. It measures 14—20 mm and can be distinguished from other tiger beetles at a glance by its entirely dark head. Like all other members of this family it is predacious, feeding chiefly on other insects as well as earthworms and even small slugs. It moves with great rapidity. Not only is it able to become airborne in a flash and fly at such speed that its passage is noticed only by the metallic glint of the dorsal part of the abdomen, but it is also capable of running so rapidly that it can capture even the fastest of prey. Like all tiger beetles it, too, has large eyes and hence also very good vision, a characteristic typical of most predators. The Wood Tiger Beetle is found only in sandy soil and only in large pine woods, where it occurs in open glades, clearings and on forest rides. The eggs are laid singly in the ground relatively early in spring. The newly-hatched larvae dig vertical burrows, the entrance to which is closed by the larva's strongly sclerotized head and prothorax, and inside which the larva is braced by the terminal segment of its abdomen and by the outgrowths on the fifth abdominal segment (1). In this position the larva lies in wait for its prey, which it captures by thrusting the front part of its body out of the burrow with lightning speed. The larva hibernates twice and the adult beetle emerges in early spring.

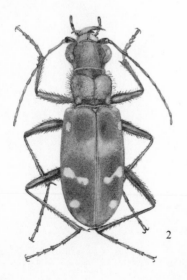

2

The larvae of most tiger beetles live in the ground in vertical subterranean burrows as shown in Fig. 1. The larvae of some Madagascar species, however, live in old tree trunks, concealing themselves in the tunnels and the escape holes made by longhorn beetles. They close these holes with their head and prothorax just as subterranean larvae do.

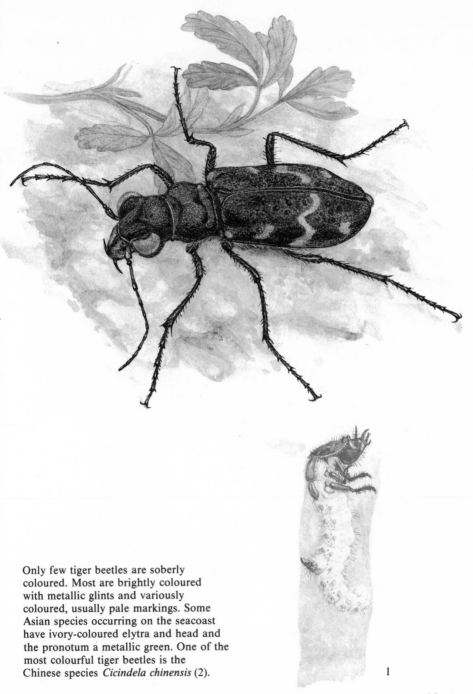

Only few tiger beetles are soberly
coloured. Most are brightly coloured
with metallic glints and variously
coloured, usually pale markings. Some
Asian species occurring on the seacoast
have ivory-coloured elytra and head and
the pronotum a metallic green. One of the
most colourful tiger beetles is the
Chinese species *Cicindela chinensis* (2).

1

Field or Green Tiger Beetle
Cicindela campestris LINNÉ, 1758

Carabidae

The 10.5—15 mm large Field Tiger Beetle is distributed throughout all of Europe, Siberia and north Africa. It occurs in several differently coloured subspecies: some are red-green, others blue to blue-violet. The upper surface of the abdomen is a very lustrous metallic blue which makes the beetle look like a flying gem when it is airborne. The Field Tiger Beetle may be encountered from early spring until October. It is particularly striking in the first truly warm spring days because it is one of the first beetles to make its appearance at this time. It occurs in sandy and loamy soils on banks and in meadows, as well as in field paths, farm tracks, balks between fields, and in sand pits, and often even within cities. The adults are among the fastest-flying of beetles but they never fly far. Generally they merely travel a few metres and come to rest again in some sunny spot. Like all tiger beetles they are also among the fastest of runners because they possess long, slender legs and also because they inhabit open land where suitable hiding places are few and far between.

Like all other tiger beetle larvae the larva of the Field Tiger Beetle is predacious, lying in wait for its prey in a vertical burrow, which may be as much as 30 cm deep. Here it remains throughout its entire life (two years), overwinters, and also pupates. The adult beetles emerge in late spring and early summer, concealing themselves deep in the ground for the winter.

The largest tiger beetles in the world are those belonging to the genus *Mantichora,* which are found in the savannas of central and south Africa. They are large, robust beetles (up to 5 cm long), and run with extreme speed. Their mandibles are modified into long, sickle-shaped organs with which they capture their prey. They feed not only on insects and insect larvae, but also on small rodents and lizards, as well as amphibians. One of the largest members

2

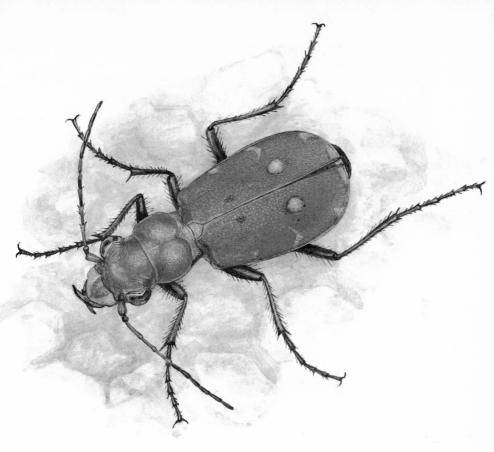

of the genus is *M. mygaloides* (1). Of interest is the ecological adaptation of tropical tiger beetles of the genus *Tricondyla*, native to the tropics of southern Asia. These beetles live on the leaves of sun-drenched trees where they also hunt their prey — other insects, mostly flies. They have lost the ability to fly and travel by running swiftly and leaping from one leaf to another. One example of such species is *T. aptera* (2).

1

This very rare but extremely interesting beetle is found throughout the Mediterranean region together with various species of ants that live in the ground. It measures 6—7 mm and stands out conspicuously amidst the tiny ants. *P. turcicus* is a typical example of a myrmecophilous or ant-loving species, so-called symphiles, totally dependent on the host ant. It is fed secretions produced by special glands and tended by the ants, which as a result often neglect the parental care of their own offspring. The beetle repays its hosts by producing a special secretion on certain parts of its body, primarily on its cup-like antennae, of which the ants are very fond and which they lick. When there are several such beetles in a single ants' nest, the ants begin to devote themselves almost exclusively to this activity, which is in fact a kind of drug addiction, cease to tend the queen and the whole colony declines — this may lead to its complete extinction or to it becoming easy prey for other, so-called slaver ant species. Adult beetles appear amongst the ants early in spring and little, practically nothing, is known about their development. The larvae are in all probability predacious and probably feed on the ant larvae; this naturally likewise contributes to the weakening of the entire ant colony. Though the adult beetle lives inside the ants' nest its whole life it has not lost the ability to fly and may even be caught with a light trap in a suitable locality. Most often, however, can it be found under stones covering the entrances to underground ants' nests.

The subfamily Paussinae is distributed in tropical and subtropical regions throughout the world. Only some of its members live in ants' nests; most tropical species live in the company of termites. Practically nothing is known about the way of life of these termitophilous species. The body is generally flat and coloured yellow-brown or brown, as in the Indian species *Platyrhopalopsis mellyi* (1). Characteristic of all members of the subfamily Paussinae are the greatly

1

modified antennae. Fig. 2 shows only
the basic types of antennae found in this
subfamily, generally with a reduced
number of segments. Practically all
antennae are widened in a bizarre
fashion or variously bent and twisted.
The glands that produce the secretion
attracting the ants or termites are
located on the antennae and body
of the beetle.

2

C. auratus is one of the loveliest and most striking beetles of the genus *Carabus*. It measures 20—28 mm and has broad longitudinal ridges on the elytra. These are the same colour as the ground colour of the elytra whereby this beetle differs from other similar species (e.g. *C. auronitens* or *C. nitens*), which have the ridges coloured black. *C. auratus* is distributed chiefly in western Europe, where in some places it is one of the commonest of the *Carabus* species, but is rare in Britain. Its eastward distribution reaches only to central Europe. The adult beetle is active during the daytime (unlike most other ground beetles of the genus *Carabus*), it prefers sandy soil and may be found in meadows, fields and gardens, where it hunts its prey — other insects, insect larvae like cockchafers, various other arthropods, slugs and earthworms. Like other ground beetles it is extremely useful in hunting chiefly harmful insects, consuming vast quantities of these pests. The eggs are laid in spring directly in the ground and the larvae hatch in 10—20 days. The larva has three larval instars, pupates in late summer, and the adult beetle emerges 2—3 weeks later, after which it hibernates. The imago may live 2—3 years. Adult beetles are very lively but only run about as they have greatly reduced wings and hence cannot fly. This wing reduction is typical for most *Carabus* species. *C. auratus* is protected by law from collectors in France and East Germany. Most European countries now have some legislation protecting ground and tiger beetles.

1

The larvae of all ground beetles of the genus *Carabus* are very similar, very active, living on the surface of the ground and beneath stones, and are always a dark colour and highly sclerotized (Fig. 1 represents the larva of *C. cancellatus*). Like the adult beetles the larvae are very useful insects in that they feed on harmful arthropods. The terminal abdominal segments bear sclerotized appendages (urogomphi) which vary in shape between species and provide diagnostic characters (2a-d).

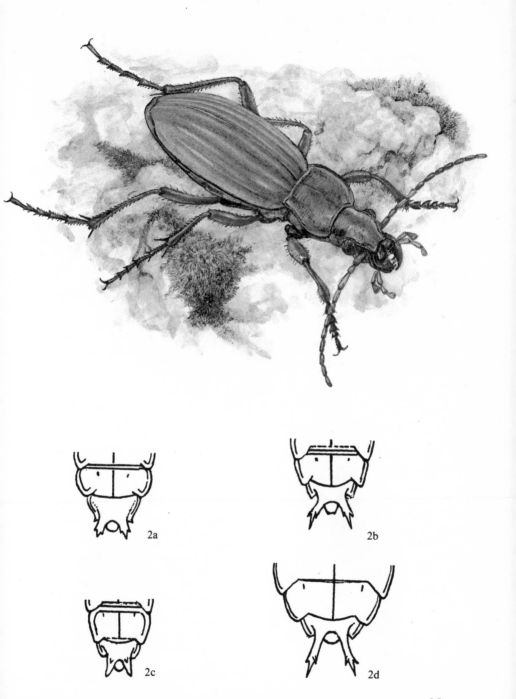

2a

2b

2c

2d

P. pilosus is a typical woodland species. It inhabits the spreading forests of the Carpathian region and may be found from median elevations up to the timberline and often even in the alpine belt. Its distribution extends westward only as far as central Europe. In western Europe it is replaced by other, similar species, which usually also have a similar ecology. *P. pilosus* is one of the most striking and handsome species of the large genus *Pterostichus* and lives in mountain forests where it can be very abundant throughout its whole distribution. It is a relatively large (15—18 mm) predacious beetle feeding chiefly on other insects and insect larvae. The larva is also predacious and lives in cracks and crevices in the ground and under stones. The eggs are laid in spring; the larva undergoes three larval instars and then pupates in summer. The adult beetle emerges in late summer and overwinters. It may be encountered throughout the spring and summer on forest rides, in meadows and in clearings on sunny days. The male can be distinguished from the female only by the enlarged front tarsi, which is a characteristic trait of all members of the ground beetle family. The number of punctures on the elytra is relatively constant in this species, only their distribution varies. Whereas most of these beetles are coloured brown, occasionally one may come across specimens that are completely metallic green or have a bluish tint.

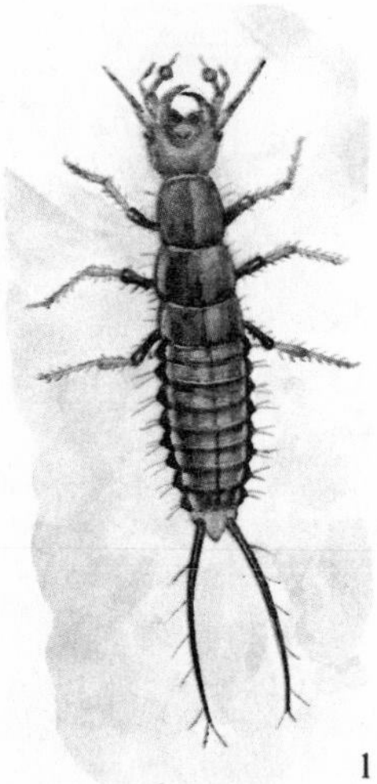

1

The larva of *P. pilosus* is very quick, slender, and not very sclerotized (it lives in the ground). Only the dorsal part of each body segment has a more greatly sclerotized area. The appendages on the last abdominal segment are relatively long, nonsclerotized and furnished with long bristles; such appendages are known as cerci. In some instances they are long, rigid and jointed, as in the larva of the small ground beetle *Loricera pilicornis* (1), which is furthermore completely sclerotized and dark, this being a common character of identification of ground beetle larvae that live on the surface of the ground.

The adult beetle of this species (2) is found by the waterside, amidst reeds and in damp localities and is one of the most abundant of the small species of ground beetles that live near water.
A striking feature of this species is the long bristles on the first six antennal segments.

Chlaenius vestitus (PAYKULL, 1790)   Carabidae

C. vestitus is another member of the ground beetle family that is widespread in central Europe. This small (8.5—11 mm) beetle is found only in very damp places, alongside rivers and ponds. It differs from the other green species of the genus *Chlaenius* by the yellow margin of the elytra which is conspicuously wider at the tip of the elytra. The latter are covered with extremely fine, thick hairs so that the beetle looks as if it were coated with a bloom. The fine hairs are typical of most species of the genus *Chlaenius* and apparently protect the beetles from getting soaked, because they often run at the very edge of the water. The eggs are laid in a very damp spot, very close to water, generally in the top layer of soil or under stones, bits of wood, etc.

The larva of *C. vestitus* is slender, quick and quite sclerotized (it lives on the surface of the soil), with long appendages (cerci) on the last abdominal segment. Development takes one year. Both the larva and the adult beetle feed on small arthropods in the vicinity of water (mites, springtails, small molluscs and small insects and insect larvae). The adult beetles are frequently attracted to light on warm summer evenings, just like many other small species of ground beetles that live near water. Other species of *Chlaenius* occur in Britain.

Another small ground beetle found only by the waterside is *Omophron limbatus* (1), which at first glance is more like a dytiscid beetle in appearance. It inhabits only the sandy banks of large rivers, lakes and flooded sand pits, where it is found by the very edge of the water, sometimes even going beneath the water's surface after food. Its almost spherical body shape enables it to move rapidly underwater as well. Though it is distributed throughout all of Europe and in north Africa, nowhere is it particularly abundant and never is it encountered in mountain districts. Another small ground beetle of the waterside is *Odocantha melanura* (2), which is found alongside large rivers

and ponds in lowland country
throughout all Europe. It likes to
overwinter in dry, upright reeds,
and this is where it is most likely
to be found. Even though
small (6—7.5 mm), it is one of the
loveliest of the European ground
beetles. It occurs in one or two localities
in southern England.

2

Bombardier Beetle
Brachinus explodens Duftschmidt, 1812   Carabidae

The Bombardier Beetle measures 4.9—8 mm and is distributed throughout southern and central Europe. In Britain there is only one species, *B. crepitans*. Like all other members of the genus *Brachinus* the Bombardier Beetle is rust-coloured with blue elytra. All bombardier beetles have an unusual form of defence. At the hind end of the abdomen they have a large paired gland from which, when they are disturbed, the beetles squirt a fluid which on contact with the air oxidizes and explodes with a popping sound and a puff of smoke. The composition of this fluid was not known for a long time. Not until the 1960s was it determined that the liquid in the abdominal segments of bombardier beetles contains hydroquinone, toluhydroquinone, hydrogen peroxide and nitrogen oxides. Peroxide is present in the gland in a concentration unknown elsewhere in the animal kingdom (a full 28 per cent). Such a concentration of peroxide acts as a virulent poison on all other organisms and presumably the main chemicals are secreted separately, coming together as they are forced out in a toxic cloud. Besides the sound effect the ejected substance is a relatively strong caustic thereby doubling the effect of the defence mechanism. The bombardier beetles' development is equally interesting. *B. explodens* inhabits sunny, dry banks and fallow land, as well as stony steppes. The eggs are laid in spring. The newly emerged larvae are small and lively and their further development takes place inside the host. Despite the abundance of this bombardier beetle scientists have as yet been unsuccessful in determining its host.

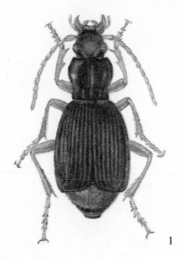

1

The complete development is known in the case of North American species of the genus *Brachinus*, whose larvae parasitize the cocoons of hydrophilids, and in the case of the related north African genus *Pteropsophus*, whose larvae attack the eggs of mole-crickets. Not even in the case of one of the largest European bombardier beetles — *Aptinus bombardus* (1) — is anything known of its development. It is a beetle typical of the beechwoods of southern Europe and when disturbed its 'bang' is so loud that it sounds like the bang of a child's cap-gun.

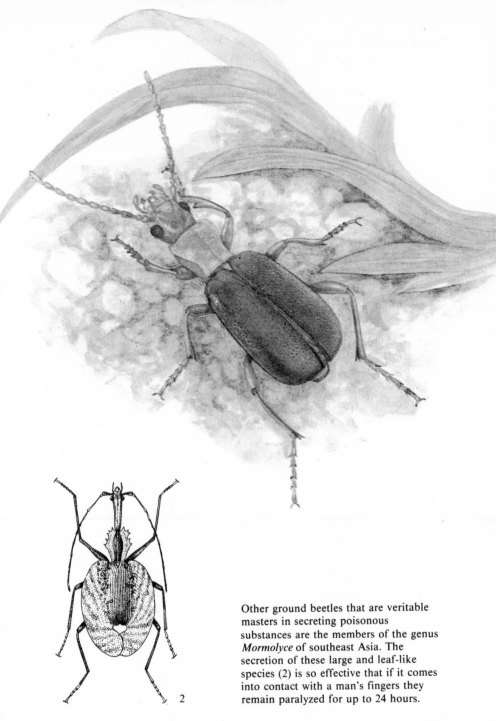

Other ground beetles that are veritable
masters in secreting poisonous
substances are the members of the genus
Mormolyce of southeast Asia. The
secretion of these large and leaf-like
species (2) is so effective that if it comes
into contact with a man's fingers they
remain paralyzed for up to 24 hours.

2

Though found throughout practically the whole of Europe, *L. chlorocephala* is not an abundant species. It is a small, 5—8 mm large beetle with metallic green head and elytra and an orange pronotum. Adult beetles live chiefly in shrubs and trees where they catch insects and insect larvae. The larvae are parasites of leaf-beetle larvae and their development is a very complex kind known as polymetaboly. The individual larval instars differ markedly from each other. The first instar (1a), known as the planidium, is very mobile, moves about freely, and actively seeks its host — the larva of a leaf-beetle. The second and third instars are parasitic. The larva of the second instar (1b), which has greatly reduced legs, develops inside the leaf-beetle larva, consumes it, and finally makes a cocoon within which develops the larva of the third instar (1c). The latter has very reduced limbs and no appendages whatsoever on the last abdominal segment. The shape is different from the typical larva of a ground beetle. Only the head and mouthparts protrude from the cocoon. It feeds on the bits of remaining tissue of the leaf-beetle larva and pupates inside the cocoon. Such a development is unusual among ground beetles but is typical for all species of the genus *Lebia*, of which there are about seven in Europe. In other beetles this type of development is found only in some rove beetles (Staphylinidae) and in all members of the Rhipiphoridae family.

1a

All members of the genus *Lebia* prefer warmer forest-steppe and scrub regions and do not occur in mountains. Found together with *L. chlorocephala* is the related and very similar species *L. cyanocephala*, which may be distinguished from the former by the coarser spotting of the elytra and darker coloration of the legs. The ecology of both species is very much the same and both are to be seen most frequently in spring and early summer.
L. cyanocephala, however, is a much rarer species and its distribution does not extend into northern Europe.

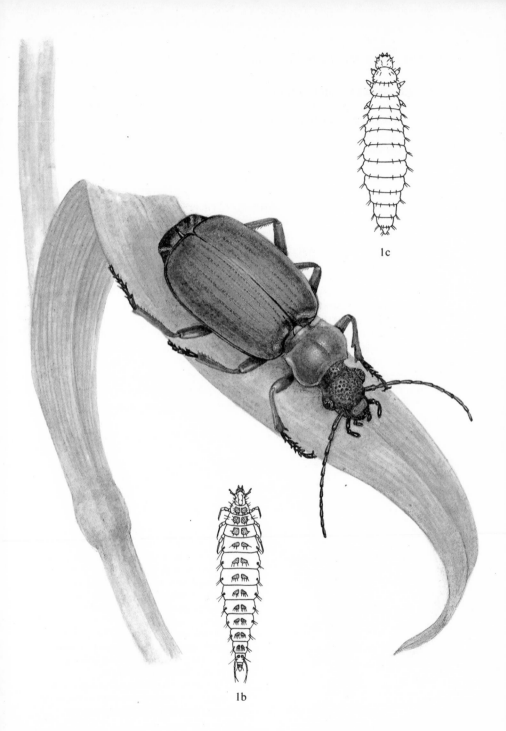

1c

1b

G. natator is the commonest of the European whirligig beetles. It measures 5—7 mm, is flat on the underside, and markedly convex above with an extraordinary silky sheen caused by the ultrafine microstructure of the elytra and pronotum. The adult beetles move swiftly about in circles or complex curves on the surface of water in lakes, ponds and swamps, as well as larger rivers. Their movement is so swift that they resemble a fast-moving, rainbow-hued marble. When danger threatens they disappear with lightning speed amidst the shoreline vegetation or beneath the water's surface. This extraordinarily rapid movement is made possible by the modified second and third pair of legs. Whereas the first pair is long and adapted for seizing prey, the other two pairs are modified and fin-like. All the leg segments are flattened and greatly widened, in addition to which they are thickly covered with hairs on the outside. The whole leg is capable of making a rapid, circling movement and functions like a miniature screw propeller. Another remarkable adaptation to life on the surface of water are the eyes (1), which are horizontally divided into two parts that are relatively far apart; the upper part for seeing over the surface and the lower for seeing down into the water. *G. natator*, as well as other members of the Gyrinidae family, is thus able to see simultaneously both above and below the water for each part of the eye is differently adapted for the different light conditions above and below the surface and the different light refraction in air and in water.

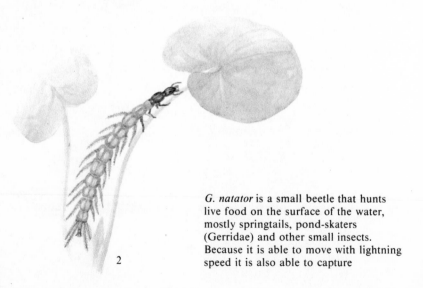

2

G. natator is a small beetle that hunts live food on the surface of the water, mostly springtails, pond-skaters (Gerridae) and other small insects. Because it is able to move with lightning speed it is also able to capture

quick-moving prey. Its larvae (2), on the other hand, are slow, dwell on the bottom, and generally feed on aquatic snails and caddis fly larvae. The eggs are laid in strands on aquatic plants. The larva is elongated and has 10 pairs of plumose abdominal tracheal gills which enable respiration underwater. When fully grown the larva climbs out of the water to pupate — usually in the ground close by the water or else on plants several centimetres above the water's surface.

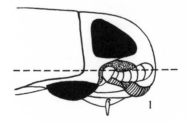

B. *elevatus* is a very common member of the Haliplidae family found in all clear, unpolluted bodies of water and slow-flowing water courses. It measures about 4—5 mm and, unlike all other water beetles, moves very slowly, hesitantly, with leisurely paddling movements of its relatively prolonged slender legs. This type of leisurely swimming movement is typical of all crawling water beetles. B. *elevatus* is generally found amidst thick aquatic vegetation or under stones in relatively shallow water. Adult beetles feed chiefly on plant food, primarily algae, but also the dead bodies of aquatic insects and other arthropods. B. *elevatus* differs from the other Haliplidae species and genera by its larger size and mainly by the longitudinal, blunt but prominent ridges on the elytra. Like all members of this family it is a good flier and on warm summer evenings it may be seen in large numbers round lamps or other sources of light located near large bodies of water.

The eggs of B. *elevatus* (like those of all other crawling water beetles) are laid on aquatic plants or inside the plant tissues. The larva, like the adult, feeds on plant and sometimes even animal food, which it sucks up into the mouth cavity through a small duct inside the hollow mandibles. The larva is elongated, cylindrical, with flat dorsal and lateral outgrowths which are apparently organs of respiration. The hind abdominal segment is furnished with relatively long appendages — cerci (1). The adult beetles hibernate along with the larvae of the last (third) instar, which pupate in spring in dry ground.

Some species of crawling water
beetles live only in absolutely clear
water in mountain districts, others, such
as *Haliplus ruficollis* (2), occur in lowland
districts in slow-flowing water courses or
ponds. This species occurs in Britain.

47

Great Water Beetle
Dytiscus marginalis LINNÉ, 1758   Dytiscidae

The Great Water Beetle is one of the largest European members of the family (it measures up to 35 mm) and definitely the best known. It is found throughout Europe in lakes and ponds with muddy bottoms and in old backwaters of large rivers. Only occasionally is it encountered in large flowing water courses. It is distinguished by marked sexual dimorphism: the female usually has deeply grooved elytra whereas the male's elytra are smooth. Furthermore the male has the first pair of tarsi greatly widened, particularly the first three segments (1). These are several times as wide as they are long and thickly covered with long hairs on the sides. In addition there are two large cup-like suction discs on the underside of the first segment that produce a thick, adhesive secretion, serving to hold the female fast during copulation, which may last as long as several hours and takes place underwater. The Great Water Beetle is very predacious. It feeds on large as well as small aquatic insects, aquatic molluscs, small crustaceans and, when given the opportunity, even on tadpoles, small frogs and small fish. For this reason it is a dreaded pest of fish-breeding ponds where its diet consists of fish fry. The Great Water Beetle (like all other predacious diving beetles) obtains oxygen from the atmosphere by breaking the water's surface with the hind end of its abdomen and literally pumping air under its raised elytra. The air supply in this subelytral cavity lasts a very long time so that there is no need for the beetle to come to the surface at frequent intervals.

1

The eggs, about 7 mm long, are laid in spring and early summer. They are deposited singly in cracks in the stems of aquatic plants, which the female either makes herself or expands with the aid of her ovipositor. The larvae, which can grow up to 70 mm long, hatch at the beginning of summer and their development takes 35—40 days, during which they undergo three larval instars. The larva of the last instar climbs out of the water and makes itself a pupal chamber in damp ground close by the water. The pupal stage lasts about

14 days and when the adult beetle
emerges it generally remains inside the
chamber where it overwinters. Although
the Great Water Beetle is a large species
its entire development takes only one
year. Adult beetles may be encountered
very early in spring.

D. latissimus is the largest European member of the Dytiscidae family. It measures up to 45 mm and is the second largest aquatic beetle in the world after the Great Silver Water Beetle (*Hydrous piceus*) of the family Hydrophilidae. It is found in large ponds, muddy lakes and spreading backwaters of large flood-plain rivers, though far more rarely than the preceding species — the Great Water Beetle. Though it is distributed more or less throughout Europe, although not in the UK, it is less common in the intensively farmed regions. The reason for this is that it is extremely sensitive to the pollution of water with the chemical substances that are increasingly being used in agriculture. Though it is perhaps even more aggressive than the Great Water Beetle and will attack even a relatively large fish or an adult frog, in view of its present rarity the damage it causes in fish-breeding ponds is negligible. The sexual dimorphism of this species is similar to that of the Great Water Beetle and its development is likewise similar. Like other predacious diving beetles *D. latissimus* is also a very good flier. Not only is its flight extremely rapid but it also covers great distances, which is quite surprising for such a large beetle. The hind legs, as in all members of this family, are modified for use as paddles. They are flattened, prolonged, and furnished with long, stiff hairs that increase the effective area of the 'paddle'.

The larvae of predacious diving beetles are brown, quite sclerotized, with a spindle-shaped body and remarkably large, usually round head distinctly separated from the thorax by a narrow 'neck'. They are even more predacious than the adult beetles, catching their prey while swimming or else lying in wait for it amidst aquatic vegetation. The tip of the abdomen is furnished either with one appendage (e.g. in *Cybister laterimarginalis*) (1) or two appendages (e.g. in *Dytiscus marginalis*) (2). Larvae of the genus *Hyphydrus* even have three abdominal appendages. The larvae of all Dytiscidae have only one pair of developed spiracles (the last pair); the others are perceptible but

non-functional. The larva obtains
oxygen by holding on to the water's
surface membrane by means of the hairs
on the terminal abdominal segments and
taking air in through the spiracle
protruding above the water.

A. sulcatus, measuring 15—18 mm, is the commonest of the medium-sized species of predacious diving beetles. It is distributed throughout all of Europe and is found in large as well as smaller ponds, slow-flowing rivers, permanent puddles and flooded sand and gravel pits. There are marked differences between the sexes in this species. The male has widened tarsi on the forelegs with well-developed suction discs and smooth elytra. The development of this species differs slightly in that the eggs are deposited in spring in small piles not in water but generally directly in the ground close to water, under wood washed up on the shore or under stones close by the water's edge. The young larva makes its way back into the water as soon as it hatches and its further development is the same as that of other diving beetle larvae. The larva is also predacious and like other related species differs from the adult in the way it obtains its food. As in all diving beetle larvae its digestion is extra-oral, for the larva's mouth opening is non-functional. It kills its prey with its long sickle-shaped mandibles through which extends a narrow duct that joins the anterior part of the alimentary canal. Through this duct it injects digestive juices from the anterior part of the alimentary canal into its prey, waits while the digestive process takes place outside its body, and then sucks out the liquefied contents of its victim — once again via the mandibular duct into the alimentary canal.

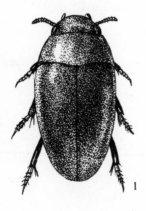

1

Noterus clavicornis (1) is relatively abundant throughout Europe in all clear water courses and bodies of water, and is often classified as a dytiscid, although it may be placed in a separate family. It is very similar to a predacious diving beetle. The larvae of this species take up oxygen in a manner that is quite different from that of other diving beetle larvae — they pierce the tissues and tap the air supply of aquatic plants to obtain the oxygen they require without having to leave the water. The suborder of carnivorous beetles (Adephaga), which has been dealt with up to this point, is followed by the small and little-known suborder Archostemata, which comprises the most primitive groups of beetles. The illustrated species *Priacma serrata* (2) belongs to the Cupedidae family, which includes several other species found in the Palaearctic.

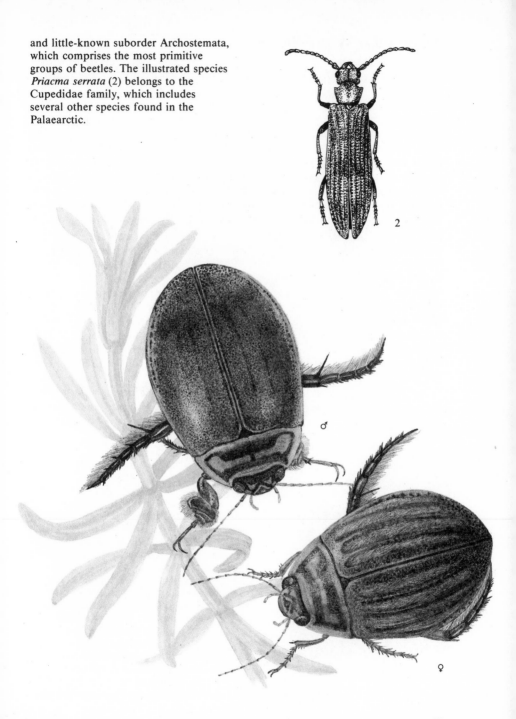

2

♂

♀

Great Silver Water-Beetle
Hydrophilus piceus LINNÉ, 1758   Hydrophilidae

The Great Silver Water-Beetle is the largest water beetle in the world. It measures up to 50 mm, is coloured black, and its body is markedly convex above and practically flat on the underside. It is distributed throughout the Palaearctic where it inhabits the muddy backwaters of large flood-plain rivers, ponds overgrown with vegetation and muddy pools. It used to be very abundant but in recent years it is becoming increasingly rare, owing to the chemical pollution of surface waters. Though it slightly resembles predacious diving beetles (Dytiscidae) and also has the second and third pair of legs adapted for paddling, it can be distinguished at a glance by the capitate antennae (terminated by a knob) and by the prominent maxillary palps which are longer than the antennae. These palps fulfil the sensory function of the antennae which in the Great Silver Water-Beetle and several related species serve as organs of respiration. Unlike the predacious diving beetles it and other Hydrophilidae obtain air by coming up head first, breaking the surface film with the sharp club-like ends of the antennae, and then guiding the air down via the antennae to the air reservoir beneath the elytra and on the underside of the abdomen. The latter is covered with fine, impermeable hairs which catch and retain a film of air. From there and from beneath the elytra the air is then channelled in a narrow band along the edge of the abdomen to the spiracles. The eggs are laid in spring in a silk-like cocoon which floats on the surface and serves to protect the eggs from enemies as well as from the adverse effects of the external environment. Such cocoons are made by all Hydrophilidae that live in water.

Unlike the adult beetles, which are phytophagous, the larvae of the Great Silver Water-Beetle, along with the larvae of predacious diving beetles, are the largest aquatic-insect predators. Their prey is the same: large aquatic insects, molluscs, tadpoles and fish-fry. Their digestion also takes place outside the body, and the digested food is sucked up into the mouth cavity. Unlike the larvae of predacious diving beetles, however, the hydrophilid larva often holds its prey above the water because its sucking mandibles are not as well adapted to this end. The larva of the

Great Silver Water-Beetle obtains
atmospheric oxygen by means of the
terminal pair of abdominal spiracles (1)
unlike the larva of another common
water scavenger beetle — *Hydrous
caraboides* (2), which obtains oxygen
from the water by means of tracheal
gills. The development of water
scavenger beetles takes one year. The
larvae always pupate in a cocoon in the
ground beyond the reach of water.

S. scarabaeoides differs from many other members of the Hydrophilidae family in that it is a terrestrial insect. It measures 5—7 mm and is distributed throughout all Europe. It is generally found on decomposing vegetable matter, chiefly in cow or horse dung. It is an important insect in animal husbandry for it serves as an intermediate host for many species of helminths whose eggs it consumes when feeding on plant remnants in dung. Cattle then devour many of these beetles along with the grass when grazing, thereby becoming infested by the helminth larvae that have developed inside the beetles in the meantime. However the beetle poses a threat not only to grazing cattle, for it is a very good flier and being attracted to light often flies at night through the lighted windows of cowsheds where it may even infect cattle that are not put out.

The female lays the eggs directly into small heaps of dung or into decomposing vegetable matter. The larva has relatively reduced legs, is lightly sclerotized and slightly resembles a small grub. Like the larvae of all terrestrial hydrophilids the larva of *S. scarabaeoides* is also phytophagous. The larva of the last instar pupates in a pupal chamber in a very damp place. So that the cocoon does not come into direct contact with water and is continually surrounded by a layer of air, the forward end of the pupa is furnished with eight long spiny processes and there are a number of similar processes on the abdomen as well (1). These spiny processes serve as struts that keep the pupa from sticking to the damp walls of the pupal chamber.

2

Hydrophilidae is the first family in the suborder Polyphaga, or carnivorous beetles — the largest beetle suborder of all. A characteristic common to all is that the first visible abdominal segment is not divided by the hind coxa. Apart from a few exceptions they are mostly terrestrial beetles and the adults are phytophagous. Closely related to the Hydrophilidae are the members of the Hydraenidae family, which includes a great many small and inconspicuous species, often with a relatively complex surface structure. One of the commonest is *Helophorus flavipes* (2), distributed

throughout practically the whole
Palaearctic region and found in
abundance in lowland as well as foothill
districts. These minute species often
swarm in vast numbers on warm spring
evenings and form a part of the
so-called aerial plankton.

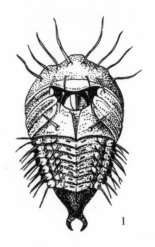

1

H. *quadrimaculatus* is distributed throughout much of the Palaearctic and is one of the more colourful members of this family. Its 7—11 mm long body is very convex and strongly sclerotized. When disturbed it presses the legs and antennae close to the body and pretends to be dead for a while. The adult beetles are saprophagous and can therefore be found in the dung of herbivores, in partly decomposed carrion, and even in decaying fungi, rotten potatoes, etc. The larva, on the other hand, is predacious, preying chiefly on the larvae of flies and other coprophagous or necrophagous insects. It is lightly sclerotized and has shortened legs and rather long mandibles, which is a typical feature of predacious beetles. The well rounded hind end of the larva's abdomen bears short, two-jointed appendages (cerci). H. *quadrimaculatus*, along with other necrophagous species, acts as a scavenger that cleans up the environment. At the same time, however, it may be an intermediate host or passive carrier of the developmental stages of helminths that infest cattle.

A characteristic of all Histeridae is the truncated elytra that leave the last two abdominal segments exposed and the short, practically geniculate antennae with a distinctly separated knob.

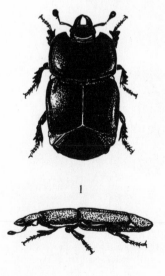

1

Some species of Histeridae are cylindrical because they are predacious, living in the tunnels of other insects, whereas many others are strongly flattened, practically leaf-like. These are mainly species that live under the bark of dying trees where they feed on the larvae of other insects. Flattened to the extreme is the body of the European species *Hololepta plana* (1) found beneath the bark of dying poplars; it is not very common, being quite absent in northern Europe.

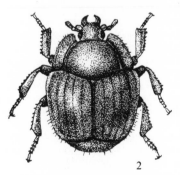

The Histeridae family also includes
myrmecophilous species, such as the
rust-coloured *Hetaerius ferrugineus* (2),
which lives in the nests of ants (chiefly
Lasius species) on warm and sunny
banks and in steppes throughout central
and southern Europe, into southern
Britain.

L. testaceus is a wingless, blind beetle without even the vestiges of eyes. It is well adapted to a very specialized way of life. This yellowish-rusty, 2—3 mm long, flat beetle lives in the fur and nests of small rodents and insectivores, chiefly voles, shrews and moles. In this instance it is the first step towards a parasitic way of life for neither the beetle nor its larva harms the host in any way whatsoever; they apparently feed on the dead surface particles of its skin but are in no way permanently tied to the host. Decomposing matter of various kinds also suffices to fill their needs. Adult beetles may be found even outside the tunnels of small mammals, in mouldy ground and beneath old, decaying leaves, where, of course, there are usually countless tunnels made by voles. *L. testaceus* has also been found in the nests of bumblebees. It is distributed throughout practically all of Europe and is rarely encountered only because of its concealed way of life. It inhabits practically every underground vole, mouse and mole nest and sometimes it is even possible to pluck adult beetles directly from the fur of small rodents caught in a trap. The larva, likewise lacking eyes, is elongated, flattened and with an abdomen composed of ten segments. The larva's antennae are three-jointed and the body is furnished with long sensory hairs, particularly at the front end. This species is most plentiful in late summer, when the adult beetles emerge from the pupae.

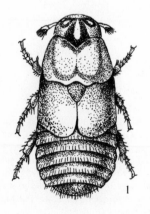

1

The family Leptinidae is relatively small; there are only 3 species in Europe. Found in the fur of beavers, both in zoos and in the wild in Europe and North America, is the Beaver Beetle (*Platypsyllus castoris*) (1). It is adapted to a parasitic way of life to a far greater degree than *L. testaceus* (abbreviated elytra, various combs and hooks for holding fast, reduced antennae) and it never leaves its host. It, too, is a pale rust colour. The third and last European species, *Silphopsyllus desmanae,* is extremely rare and lives in the fur of the Russian Desman (*Desmana moschata*).

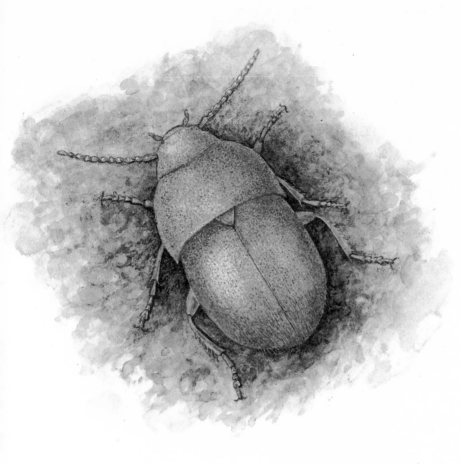

The nests of birds as well as mammals, decomposing matter, fungi and dung, etc. are inhabited by beetles of the related Catopidae family, whose presence there is not immediately evident. The most common of the European species is *Catops nigrita* (2), measuring about 3.5—4.5 mm, found in large numbers chiefly on carrion.

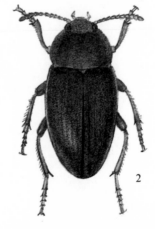

2

61

Common Sexton or **Burying Beetle**
Nicrophorus vespillo (LINNÉ, 1758)   Silphidae

The Common Burying Beetle measures up to 22 mm, and is brightly coloured in orange and black. It is common and found practically throughout Europe. The elytra are shortened at the tip so that the last three abdominal segments are free and visible. This is a character common to all burying beetles of the genus *Nicrophorus*. They are extremely useful in that they dispose of the dead bodies of animals and are truly beneficial scavengers. The Common Burying Beetle has a very well developed sense of smell located in the widened joints of the antennae and can smell carrion in the first stages of decay from a considerable distance. Large numbers of beetles may collect round a single dead animal. If the corpse is resting on hard ground the beetles slowly move it (if it is not too big) to more suitable, softer ground where they begin to loosen and excavate the soil from under the corpse, which slowly but surely sinks into the ground. At this point the largest female begins chasing the other beetles away and only a single pair remains to complete the burial. Only when the corpse is completely covered with soil does the female begin laying the yellow, elongate eggs nearby. The larvae that hatch from the eggs are plump with short legs and coloured yellow with brown spiny sclerites (1). They move slowly and at first glance slightly resemble large ant larvae. The hind end of the body bears a pair of stout, sclerotized appendages — urogomphi.

1

All species of the genus *Nicrophorus* are noted for their parental care. After laying the eggs the female generally drives away even the male and before the larvae hatch (after about 5 days), she rolls the corpse up into a kind of ball with a funnel-shaped crater at the top. This she fills with digestive juices secreted by her alimentary tract and then closes it. When the larvae emerge they gather round this depression and are fed digested food from the crater by the mother from mouth to mouth at short intervals (10—30 minutes). After being fed thus for several hours the larvae begin to feed by themselves. The entire process is repeated at the beginning of the second instar. Only the third and final larval instar feeds itself completely without the mother's aid. The pupal stage lasts about 2 weeks. In some species the larvae of the third instar overwinter, in others it is the adult beetles.

D. quadripunctata, unlike most carrion beetles, which are mainly black or with orange markings at the most, is yellow-brown with the head and centre of the pronotum coloured black and with four black round spots on the elytra. This beetle (12—14 mm) is found in warmer regions throughout Europe. It is a very good flier. It does not feed on carrion like most members of this family but is predacious. Adult beetles and above all the larvae are important predators of caterpillars, mainly Tortrix and Lymantrid Moth larvae, which they are capable of consuming in unbelievable quantities. The larva (1) is black with the head and tip of the abdomen coloured rusty-brown, its body flattened, strongly sclerotized and slightly resembling a trilobite in shape. Its legs are relatively short and the abdominal segments extend out and backward in the form of flattened spines. The larvae undergo three larval instars and their development is very rapid (lasting 4—5 weeks). They pupate in the ground. Normally they are encountered only on occasion but during the hibernating period of certain moth larvae (e.g. the larvae of the Green Oak Tortrix Moth — *Tortrix viridana*) they may be found in vast numbers running about on the trunks and branches of trees and bushes in pursuit of the caterpillars. Because of this feeding specialization *D. quadripunctata* is one of the most useful and beneficial of all beetles.

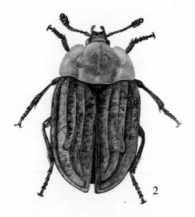

Another of nature's important scavengers is *Oiceoptoma thoracica* (2). It is entirely black with a velvety orange pronotum and is one of the commonest members of the Silphidae family in Europe, where it occurs from lowland to high mountain elevations. The larvae resemble those of *D. quadripunctata* but are entirely black-brown and even more greatly flattened.

Related to the carrion beetles is the peculiar family Bathyscidae, whose members inhabit the caves of southern

Europe. Because they live in eternal
darkness they are blind and have lost
the ability to fly. Their elytra are usually
bizarrely inflated (e.g. in the genus
Bathysca) (3), and the legs and antennae
are long and filiform. Because of their
lengthy isolation the species that have
evolved in each system of caves are all
different.

1

3

An incredible number of beetle species, especially small ones, live on fungi. One such family that specializes almost exclusively in this way of life (so-called mycetophagy) is the Anisotomidae family, which comprises mostly small and practically hemispherical species. The species most commonly found in Europe is *A. humeralis*. It is a 3—4 mm long, black and very-convex beetle with two red patches on the elytra. Very occasionally these spots may be absent or, vice versa, the elytra may be entirely red. This beetle is found in all forests from lowland to mountain elevations. It occurs primarily on harder species of wood fungi (mainly bracket fungi) or the hard sclerotia of slime moulds (Myxomycetes). The larvae of *A. humeralis* have flattened, pale coloured bodies, and live inside fungus tissues. Perhaps the fungus this species is most fond of is the bracket fungus *Polyporus squamosus* which, when it is dying, ferments and has a powerful stench that attracts thousands of widely varied beetles. *A. humeralis* is a good flier and whole swarms of these beetles may be encountered in suitable localities particularly on warm summer evenings. As a matter of fact all Anisotomidae form a substantial part of the aerial plankton, which is an enormous quantity of small species of insects and other arthropods that under favourable weather conditions are carried up into the air and serve as food for many other animals.

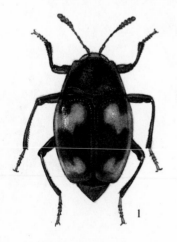

1

Other mycetophagous beetles include *Scaphidium quadrimaculata* (1) of the Scaphididae family, which lives on various soft fungi and on the mycelia of fungi beneath the bark of trees and tree stumps. Moulds and fine mycelia are the specialty of beetles of the Scydmaenidae family, which are 1.2—2.5 mm long, black or rust-coloured beetles shaped like a tear-drop. Some species have greatly developed maxillary palps, e.g. *Scydmaenus tarsatus* (2). The members of the small but interesting Leiodidae family live on underground fungi (truffles). Some species (e.g. *Liodes calcarata*) (3) have the tibiae strongly curved and covered thickly with spines, which makes them well adapted for digging underground.

2

3

All members of this family are small, dark or rust-coloured and relatively uniform. A typical characteristic is the truncated elytra that leave the last 4 to 5 abdominal segments exposed. Most species live in mouldy matter under bark, in old mouldy leaves, or in the crumbling wood of old trees and tree stumps. These sites are where one will also find a typical representative of the family — *R. longicornis*. It is a small (1.8—2.2 mm), rust-coloured beetle resembling an ant in shape. It has long slender antennae terminated by an insignificant knob. The maxillary palps, especially those of males, are prolonged and their terminal segment is enlarged. *R. longicornis* is distributed throughout all Europe, north Africa and Central Asia.

Some members of this family may be found also in the mouldy lining of birds' nests, in the nests of small mammals and in the nests of social bees and wasps; other species live in ants' nests either as tolerated or pampered quests. The latter produce a secretion on the exposed abdominal segments which the ants like to lick. The family also includes species that live freely in the soil alongside flowing water, e.g. *Biblioplectus ambiguus* (1). These beetles have an elongated body resembling that of the rove beetles (Staphylinidae), to which they are closely related.

The larvae of the Pselaphidae family are practically unknown. The larva of the only species studied to date resembles the larva of rove beetles.

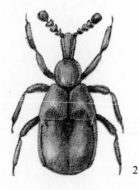

2

Another pselaphid beetle is the pale rust-coloured, 2 mm long *Claviger testaceus* (2). It is a myrmecophilous species that lives as a symphile in the company of the yellow ant *Lasius flavus*. Its parasitic way of life has brought about marked adaptations: it has lost the ability to fly, is entirely blind, and has a reduced number of tarsal segments as well as a reduced number and

thickening of the antennal segments. On the dorsal side of the abdomen, right behind the elytra, is a deep depression surrounded by long hairs where the secretion that attracts the ants is produced. It is found throughout Europe including the UK and is completely dependent on its host ants.

1

The characteristic that distinguishes *E. hirtus* from other large and colourful rove beetles is its dense coat of long hairs. The head, pronotum and last three abdominal segments are thickly covered with long, yellow hairs. In other rove beetles the head and pronotum are always bare or only sparsely bristled. *E. hirtus* measures 18—28 mm and its sickle-shaped mandibles indicate its predacious way of life. It feeds on the larvae of other insects, chiefly those of flies. It is extremely quick and hunts its prey mostly beneath the carcasses of large animals and beneath larger heaps of dung on pastureland where cattle graze. Here it also hunts the larvae of various scarabaeid beetles, of which there is always an ample supply. Another artificial biotope are the tips near slaughterhouses where bones and refuse are dumped. In such a place this beetle, though otherwise relatively rare, may even be found in great numbers. The larva of *E. hirtus* lives in much the same way as the adult beetle. This species is found throughout the warm regions of central and southern Europe but in all places it is relatively rare. Concealed beneath the greatly shortened elytra are fully developed wings (as in all rove beetles). *E. hirtus* flies extremely well with its abdomen slightly uptilted — a flight position adopted by all rove beetles.

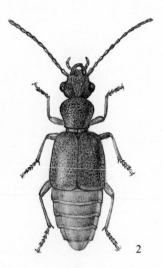

2

The family Staphylinidae has the largest number of species. Some 30,000 have been described to date. Characteristic features are shortened elytra and head pointing straight forward (prognathous). The elytra are generally so truncated that the entire abdomen is exposed. However in some species, e.g. of the genus *Anthobium*, only the last two abdominal segments are exposed.

Rove beetles of the subfamily
Micropeplinae are noted for the
handsome structure of the pronotum,
elytra and abdominal segments. They
also have the number of antennal
segments reduced to nine and the
antennae terminated by a prominent
knob. One of the most common is the
2 mm long *Micropeplus porcatus* (1), which
lives in compost and rotting leaves. An
exception amongst the otherwise mostly
predacious or saprophagous rove beetles
is the genus *Anthophagus,* whose
members, e.g. *A. caraboides* (2), feed on
parts of flowers.

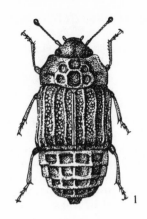

1

S. caesareus is distributed throughout all of southern and central Europe and partly also in northern Europe. It occurs under stones, pieces of wood or bark in open as well as forest-steppe country. It differs from all related species by its size (17—22 mm) and striking coloration. The yellow patches on the dorsal side of the abdominal segments are characteristic. Adult beetles run about nimbly in the evening or after a rainfall and may be found even on agricultural land. Like most rove beetles, *S. caesareus* is also predacious, preying on other insects and insect larvae, earthworms and small snails. The larva is predacious too and lives under stones and in cracks in the soil. It is long, slender and cylindrical (1), and greatly resembles certain ground beetle (Carabidae) larvae. Only the head and thorax are more strongly sclerotized; the abdominal segments are soft and pale with sclerotized plates on the dorsal side. The last abdominal segment bears two long appendages — cerci. Larval development consists of three larval instars; the larva of the third instar hibernates.

1

It was discovered that the development of certain parasitic rove beetles (e. g. of the genus *Aleochara*) was characterized by polymetaboly: the larva of the first instar is active and seeks the pupae of cycloraph flies. On penetrating the pupa it changes into an inactive larva that completes its development inside the pupa it entered. The pupa of these rove beetles is a mummy-like obtect pupa, a kind only very occasionally found in ·beetles.

Other species of rove beetles, e.g. of the genus *Bledius*, that live beside water are noted for their parental care. Before laying the eggs the female excavates a long tunnel in the sand, digs small chambers off this tunnel and provisions them with food (algae), after which she deposits a single egg in each chamber.

Many species of rove beetles may also be found on fungi, chiefly the minute species of the large genus *Atheta*, which are only 1—2 mm long and feed there on mites and springtails. Another is the colourful *Oxyporus rufus* (2), which measures up to 12 mm and feeds on fly larvae in fungi. It is widely distributed across the whole of Europe and the Caucasus to Siberia.

2

Often encountered on the sandy banks of rivers and ponds is the colourful *P. riparius,* a slender and very nimble rove beetle about 8 mm long. The head and tip of the abdomen are black, the elytra azure blue and the remainder of the body orange. It differs from other related species in that its pronotum is as long as it is wide. *P. riparius* is distributed throughout most of Europe. It is found by the edge of water in cracks and under stones, as well as under aquatic plants and wood washed up on the shore, where it hunts small insects, insect larvae and mites. The larva is also predacious, very nimble, longish-cylindrical and reminiscent of the larvae of small ground beetles; it differs from the latter by having a rounded head. The last abdominal segment bears long unjointed appendages. The striking, warning coloration of this beetle (as well as other beetles of the genus *Paederus*) indicates that it is a poisonous species. The effective principle called 'paederin' is an alkaloid. It is a contact poison that has a blistering effect. It is dispersed in the haemolymph and thus the whole beetle is poisonous. If the beetle is handled carelessly and squashed nothing is visible on the skin at first, nor is there any particular sensation. Only after several hours or even two days do blisters appear. These heal slowly and last a number of days. If this rove beetle flies into a person's eye it may cause serious damage to the eye and conjunctiva.

A large number of rove beetles became adapted to living with ants. Typical European examples are *Atemeles strumosus* (1), *Dinarda dentata* (2), and *Zyras humeralis* (3).

Myrmecophilous species are either 'pampered guests' (symphiles) or more frequently indifferently 'tolerated guests' (synoeketes), but in most cases they are treated with hostility (synechthrans). Most of these myrmecophilous rove beetles belong to the subfamily Aleocharinae. Synechthrans feed on ant eggs, larvae and pupae and defend themselves against the ants by means of various foul-smelling secretions which they exude on various parts of the

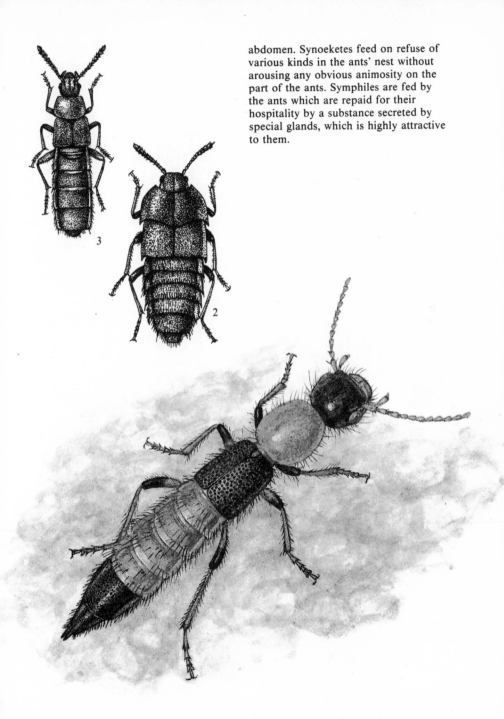

abdomen. Synoeketes feed on refuse of various kinds in the ants' nest without arousing any obvious animosity on the part of the ants. Symphiles are fed by the ants which are repaid for their hospitality by a substance secreted by special glands, which is highly attractive to them.

Stag Beetle
Lucanus cervus LINNÉ, 1758   Lucanidae

The Stag Beetle is the largest (males are up to 75 mm long) and probably the best known European beetle, its distribution extending from the south of the continent to southern Scandinavia. It inhabits old deciduous forests where it is found in rotting trees, in which the eggs are laid in late spring and early summer. The larva develops in the rotting wood of these trees and tree stumps. The Stag Beetle prefers oak woods but its development may also take place in other broad-leaved trees, mainly beech, maple, willow and elm. Development lasts 5—8 years and always takes place in the root stock. The larva has three instars; the larva of the last instar pupates in a large cocoon which it makes from crumbling wood. The adult beetle emerges in late summer but remains inside the cocoon and overwinters there. Mating takes place in spring, generally in May. During the courtship the males engage in symbolic duels, the purpose of which is merely to throw their opponent off the branch or out of the tree. Hardly ever does the rival suffer any harm. A favourite food of Stag Beetles is the fermenting sap oozing from bruised broad-leaved trees. On warm evenings whole clusters of Stag Beetles converge on such trees literally becoming intoxicated on the sap.

Southeastern Europe is the home of another stag beetle — *Lucanus turcicus* — which can be identified by the six lamellae on the distal segment of antennae.

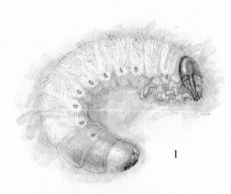

1

The Stag Beetle larva (1) has a body curved in the form of a letter C and is relatively inactive. If there are too many larvae in a single stump or tree they become cannibalistic and some are devoured by the others.

The differences between the sexes in the Stag Beetle include not only the well developed mandibles in the males, but also differences in the shape of the head and the pronotum. The males exhibit great variability in size as well as in the length and strength of the mandibles and also in the proportions of the head. In a single locality one may find huge males with exaggeratedly enlarged mandibles (2) side by side with small males whose mandibles are only slightly

prolonged (3). This variability is caused by the larva's diet. If the rotting wood it feeds on is too dry or too greatly decomposed and humusy the resulting beetle, a so-called hungry form, is much smaller and weaker than normal individuals.

S. cylindricum is found in the larger forests of mountain and foothill districts throughout Europe and may serve as a kind of indicator of the biotope, for it feeds mainly on well established beech woods. It is a 12—16 mm long, cylindrical beetle with marked differences between the sexes. The male has a prominent, blunt, recurved horn on the head furnished on the edge with rust-coloured hairs. The front half of the pronotum is deeply hollowed and the depression is edged with flat lamellae and teeth. The female has no outgrowths on the head and the depression in the pronotum is much shallower with a simple lamellate margin. Like all stag beetles this species is also very slow and cumbersome in flight. These small beetles appear very early in spring when mating takes place. In spring the female deposits the eggs in cracks and crevices in the trunks and thick branches of dead beeches. The larva excavates tunnels filled with coarse particles of rotting wood and has three larval instars. Its development generally takes three years, but may take even longer in unfavourable conditions (for example if the substrate becomes excessively dry). The larva of the last instar pupates in summer in a pupal chamber close below the surface of the trunk and the adult beetle emerges in late summer; however it does not leave the pupal chamber and overwinters there.

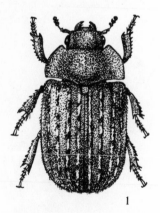

1

Stag beetles, Lucanidae, are found more abundantly in the tropics, where there are hundreds of different species. The Oriental region is rich in species as well as bizarre forms, while Europe has only 10 species. One of these, *Aesalus scarabeaoides* (1), does not even look like a stag beetle. There is no difference between the male and female — both are small and coloured rusty-brown. The larva is found in the reddish rotting wood of old oaks and oak stumps. It is distributed in warm regions in central and southern Europe.

♀

♂

This beetle is one of the most common members of the genus *Aphodius* in Europe and at the same time one of the most plentiful of all coprophagous beetles. It is small, measuring only 4—5 mm, and its yellow elytra have extremely variable markings composed of tiny black dots. It is distributed throughout all Europe, in Asia Minor and in the USA, where it is found from lowland districts to fairly high up in the mountains in meadows, steppes and pastureland as well as distinctly farming country. It feeds on the dung of all herbivores but exhibits a marked preference for horse dung. The eggs are laid in dung already very early in spring. The larva is grub-like and there are three larval instars. When weather conditions are favourable there may be two generations during the spring and summer. The larvae live directly in the dung without any parental care. The adults of the second generation overwinter in the ground beneath old heaps of dung. *A. distinctus* along with *A. fimetarius*, another very plentiful species which has entirely red elytra, is very important, because of its large numbers, in removing excrement in the wild. Furthermore they also provide a rich source of food for birds that occur in pasturelands. On the other hand, of course, *A. distinctus* is one of the commonest intermediate hosts of various helminths that infest livestock, chiefly cestode worms in the case of cattle and acanthocephalan worms in the case of pigs.

In Europe there are about 80 species of *Aphodius*, some of which do not live in dung at all. Their larvae develop in decaying vegetable matter, in mouldy leaves and the like. Certain other beetles related to *Aphodius* likewise live in sandy soil on rotting vegetation. Their legs are adapted for burrowing and are variously sculptured on the surface. Examples are *Rhyssemus germanus* (1), *Psammodius sulcicollis* (2), *Oxyomus silvestris* (3) and *Psammophorus sabuleti* (4). Published recently was a case of parasitism by one species of *Aphodius* in the rectums of children in India. It is unlikely that this is an instance of true parasitism because the species in question

is commonly found freely in the dung of herbivores. It would seem that the beetles entered the children's rectums when the youngsters were playing on the ground in conditions that were far from hygienic.

This scarab beetle was already known and held sacred in ancient Egypt as testified to by numerous archeological finds. It is 25— 35 mm long and is distributed throughout the Mediterranean region, its range extending to central Europe and to central Asia. It is found in steppe, forest-steppe and semi-desert regions wherever there are ample numbers of large herbivores, on whose dung it feeds. Because it lives in dry districts where its food soon dries up, it rolls the dung into a ball up to several centimetres in diameter which it then transports to a hiding place and only when it is safely stored does it begin to consume it. When forming the ball and rolling it away it works primarily with its hind legs while standing head down on its forelegs. Unlike these food balls, which are perfectly spherical, the balls of dung in which the eggs are laid are pear-shaped. The dung is kneaded into this shape by the female when it is safely underground, in a brood chamber, where the entire larval development takes place. There are altogether three larval instars. Inasmuch as the walls of the pear-shaped food ball are firmed either with soil or with a secretion, when the entire food supply is consumed there remains a hollow pear-shaped structure, partly filled with the larva's faeces, in which the larva also pupates. *S. sacer* has a well developed sense of smell and flies to dung from considerable distances. In semi-desert regions it is not uncommon for a flock of goats or sheep or a herd of camels on the march to be followed by a whole cloud of scarab beetles that immediately converge on every bit of fresh dung left by the animals.

1

Other species of coprophagous scarabaeid beetles are found in Europe, e. g. about 40 species of the genus *Onthophagus*. The males generally have variously shaped paired or unpaired horns and processes. A feature common to the genus is highly developed brood care. For example the female *O. nuchicornis* (1), often with the aid of the male, digs near a heap of dung a corridor often several centimetres long with simple or branching side galleries (2). At the end of each gallery she constructs a barrel-shaped brood chamber containing a supply of dung (3) where the typically 'hump-backed' larva (4) then develops. This type of larva is typical of all members of the subfamily Coprinae.

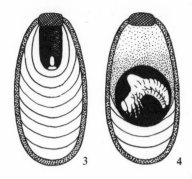

3   4

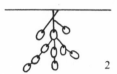

2

Common Cockchafer or May Beetle
Melolontha melolontha (LINNÉ, 1758)   Scarabaeidae

The Common Cockchafer was one of the most dreaded beetle pests of agriculture until recent years. It measures up to 30 mm and is distributed throughout practically all of Europe excepting the Iberian peninsula and northern Scandinavia. The adult beetle is destructive to a great variety of broad-leaved trees and when its population reaches plague numbers it causes the complete defoliation of trees. In spring the female (which can be distinguished from the male by the much smaller and shorter 'fan' composed of lamellae on the terminal antennal segments) lays batches of 15—30 eggs in the ground at a depth of 10—30 centimetres. The eggs are yellow or creamy-white and about 3 mm long. The larvae, which hatch after a short time (Fig. 1 shows the larva of *M. hippocastani*), devour the roots of all sorts of cultivated crops, generally cereal and vegetable crops and in southern Europe also grape vines. Under ideal conditions the larva overwinters twice and the third larval instar pupates in August. The adult beetle emerges in late summer but remains in the pupal cell where it hibernates. Early the following May the adults appear in swarms. Under unfavourable conditions or in the northern parts of Europe the development may take as long as four or five years. Under ideal conditions, however, the cockchafer's development may be so synchronized that the beetles appear in enormous numbers every third year. Such years are then called 'cockchafer years'.

1

Cockchafers are mentioned as pests already in the writings of Aristotle and Pliny and medieval records contain numerous reports about the defoliation caused by the adult beetles as well as the damage caused by the larvae, which were called 'white worm'. In the 1950s and 1960s, however, an organized effort was mounted to combat this pest by means of chemical agents based chiefly on DDT and HCH. Since then 'cockchafer years' are nonexistent and in most of Europe the Common Cockchafer is hardly to be seen at all. Spraying with chemical agents, however, destroyed many other insects and along with these also many birds and insectivores.

84

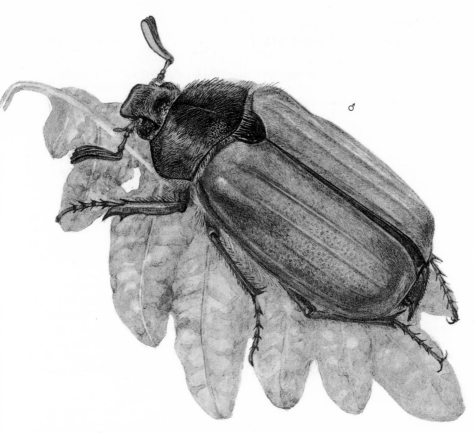

♂

In central and southern Europe there are altogether three species of cockchafers distinguished from one another by the shape of the terminal abdominal segment or pygidium. They are the Common Cockchafer (*Melolontha melolontha*) (2), the even more rarely seen *M. hippocastani* (3), and the rarest *M. pectoralis* (4).

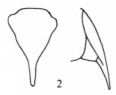

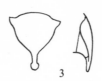

Walker
Polyphylla fullo (LINNÉ, 1758)   Scarabaeidae

This chafer, the largest European member of the subfamily Melolon-
thinae, is a robust 25—35 mm long beetle with a striking black and
brown marbled pattern. The male is readily distinguished from the
female by the huge, curved antennal fan, formed by the seven distal
segments of the antennae. *P. fullo* is distributed throughout all central
and southern Europe and extends to Scandinavia and to the Ukraine.
It is found in warm lowland and foothill districts and occurs only in
sandy soil, in which the female lays 25—40 eggs, usually by the edge
of pine woods or vineyards, from June to August. The development
of the egg takes about four weeks and the larval development comprises three larval instars. First to hibernate is the larva of the first instar which does not moult until the following spring or summer. The
second year the larva of the second instar hibernates and the third
year the larva of the third instar; the latter, however, may hibernate
once again before pupating. The larval development thus takes 3—4
years. The larva feeds on the roots of grasses and above all of young
pine trees and is hence a pest of forest nurseries and vineyards located on sandy soil. The pupal stage lasts approximately three weeks
and the adult beetles emerge, often in large numbers, in late June or
more commonly in July. The adult beetles are crepuscular and always
fly after sunset, often until late at night. They are also attracted to
light and hence often occur in swarms round strong sources of light.

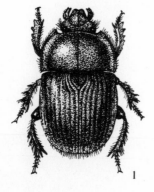

Members of the subfamily of dung
beetles (Geotrupinae) are generally
coprophagous species with greatly
developed brood care. *Geotrupes
stercorarius* (1) is a woodland species.
The female digs a vertical shaft in the
ground below dung which may be up to
40 cm long and has several side shafts;
these she fills with dung in which she
then lays the eggs. The larva (2) is
a typical grub but, unlike the larvae of
true scarab beetles of the subfamily
Scarabaeinae, it does not have a 'hump'
on the dorsal side of the thorax. The
development of the larva takes one year

and the adult beetle must overwinter once more before it is capable of reproduction. Another phytophagous scarab beetle is the species *Lethrus apterus* (3) whose larvae feed in the brood chambers on vine leaves. This species is a pest in vineyards.

2

3 ♂

Garden Chafer
Phyllopertha horticola (Linné, 1758) Scarabaeidae

The Garden Chafer is another economically important species. This approximately 10 mm long beetle is distributed throughout Europe and central Asia, extending eastward through Siberia and Mongolia as far as the Pacific. Adult beetles often occur in vast numbers from May till July (the higher the altitude above sea level, the later they appear). In some parts of central Europe this species may be encountered even above the upper limit of the forest. Adult beetles feed chiefly on the flowers of fruit-trees and rose-bushes as well as on the foliage of a number of broad-leaved trees. In June and July the female lays 15—30 eggs in the ground at a depth of 5—20 cm. The larvae hatch in about three weeks and feed on the roots of cultivated crops, chiefly cereal grains. There are three larval instars. The entire life cycle of the Garden Chafer takes 1—3 years in northern Europe, while in the climatic conditions of central Europe it usually takes two years. The larvae migrate vertically in the soil during the year — similarly to Common Cockchafer larvae. This is dependent on rainfall and on the season of the year. During the summer when there is ample rainfall the larva stays only 5—10 cm below the surface whereas in dry periods or when hibernating it descends to a depth of 30 cm. Chemical agents based on DDT and HCH were used to combat this species but in far smaller measure and with much less success than in the case of the Common Cockchafer.

Related to the Garden Chafer are several other genera in Japan and the Far East, e.g. the large genus *Popilia*, which also includes several very serious agricultural pests. In Europe there are primarily the genus *Anisoplia* and the

genus *Anomala*. The genus *Anisoplia* is
distinguished by the snout-like clypeus
(1). *A. segetum* (2) is a plentiful species
in southern Europe where it causes
damage to cereals. Its larvae develop in
sandy soil. Several other species, mainly
central and south European species,
belong to the genus *Anomala*. These are
plump, robust and markedly convex
beetles often with bright metallic
coloration. *A. dubia* (3) has a similar life
cycle to the Garden Chafer but is rarer
and not a major agricultural pest.

3

European Rhinoceros Beetle
Oryctes nasicornis (LINNÉ, 1758)   Scarabaeidae

This is one of the largest European beetles. It is 20—40 mm long, glossy chestnut brown, and distributed throughout all Europe, north Africa and a large part of central Asia. It is found in lowland and warm foothill districts where it occurs in forest-steppe biotopes and open, sun-dappled deciduous woods, mainly oak woods. It is also found in larger parks in cities but is encountered only occasionally because it is a crepuscular species that is active only after sunset. The eggs — oval, up to 0.5 cm long and yellowish — are laid in the rotting wood of tree stumps, old broad-leaved trees and dead roots or in compost, hotbeds and old mouldy sawdust. The larva has three larval instars and is the largest beetle larva in Europe. The fully-grown larva of the last instar measures up to 12 cm; it is dingy white with the body curved in the form of a letter C (typical grub) and has a strongly sclerotized, dark head. Larval development takes 3—5 years. The larva of the third instar pupates in a cocoon cemented together with soil, bits of wood or sawdust. The cocoon is the size of a hen's or duck's egg. The adult beetle overwinters in the cocoon and does not leave it until late spring of the following year. Nowadays this beetle is most likely to be found in large sawmills, where there are years-old piles of sawdust and stripped-off bark. The increasing use of chemical fertilizers and sprays has caused a decline in its presence in the large compost heaps of horticultural establishments where it used to be very plentiful.

2 ♂

Most species of the subfamily Dynastinae, to which the European Rhinoceros Beetle also belongs, exhibit marked sexual dimorphism. The male has a long, recurved horn on the head and on the pronotum a hollow topped by two prominent protuberances. In tropical members of this subfamily the appearance of the males is sometimes even more bizarre. Such is the case in the male of *Allomyra dichotomus* (1), found in the Far East and in China. One of the largest beetles in the world,

Dynastes hercules (2), measuring up to 15 cm and found in the Antilles and northern South America, has on the pronotum a long, forward-pointing horn that extends far beyond the head, and on the underside of this horn a line of thick rust-coloured hairs.

Rose Chafer
Cetonia aurata (LINNÉ, 1758)

Scarabaeidae

The Rose Chafer is a 15—20 mm long beetle coloured golden-green, in southern Europe sometimes green-violet. Its range embraces all Europe extending eastward to central Asia. It is found from lowland to relatively high mountain districts and its larvae develop in the rotting wood of tree stumps and old hollow trees. Often the larvae may be found also in compost heaps and hotbeds. Larval development includes three instars and takes 1—2 years. Prior to pupating the larva of the last instar begins exuding from the anus a mushy substance which it spreads with the aid of its mandibles and maxillae on bits of soil and pieces of wood in its immediate vicinity. With squirming, rotating movements it compresses this matter and once again coats it with its cement. In this manner it fashions a cocoon measuring about 25 mm and perfectly smooth inside, within which the larva finally pupates. Adult beetles are fond of sun and warmth. During the hottest part of the day they fly about rapidly, coming to rest now and then on flowers, chiefly on flowering rose, elder, thistles and various umbelliferous plants as well as on bruised trees exuding sap. When disturbed the beetles often withdraw their legs and feign death (so-called thanatosis).

Some European species of Cetoniinae, mainly of the genus *Potosia,* develop in ants' nests. Their larvae may then be found at the edge of large anthills where they feed on vegetable remnants.

2

Another European species of Cetoniinae is *Tropinota hirta* (1); a typical characteristic of this beetle is its long, wavy pubescence. It is found throughout Europe in lowland and hilly country. The larva develops in the ground, where it generally feeds on dead plant roots and decaying plant remnants. Adult beetles fly from April till June; they visit a wide variety of flowers, with a special predilection for yellow blossoms, as well as flowering hawthorn and fruit trees.

Another common chafer in the
subfamily Trichiinae is *Trichius fasciatus*
(2) a mountainous species in central
Europe and found in northern Britain.
Its behaviour and colour mimic bumblebees, particularly noticeable when it
alights on flowers. The larvae develop in
decaying hardwood.

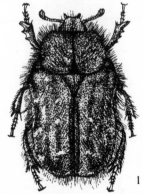

1

Valgus hemipterus is only 6—10 mm long, greatly flattened above and angular in outline. It is distributed throughout all Europe excepting Scandinavia and Britain, eastward to the Caucasus and in north Africa. It is found primarily in lowland and warm hilly country and is one of the first beetles to be seen on flowers in spring. It is a very plentiful species. The adult beetles like warmth and sunshine and fly nimbly about in warm weather. The male is distinguished from the female by the more pronounced markings on the elytra and the pronotum. The female has the terminal abdominal segment (pygidium) prolonged into a lance-like spine. The eggs are generally laid in May and early June in the dead wood of broad-leaved trees, mostly willows, poplars and fruit trees. As a rule the bark or outer layer of wood of these tree trunks or stumps is still hard and the female's 'ovipositor' serves to deposit the eggs deep into the cracks of the outer layer so that the newly hatched larvae are as close to the decayed wood inside as possible. The larval development takes one year and the fully grown larva pupates in late summer in a small chamber at the end of a tunnel, which it excavates previously. The adult beetle emerges in autumn of the same year but overwinters inside the pupal chamber and does not leave it until the following spring.

This is the only European member of the genus *Valgus*. Dozens of brightly coloured species are found mainly in southeast Asia, which is also the evolutionary centre of the entire subfamily Valginae.

Species of the large genus *Trox* feed on dried animal material, hoof, horn, skin etc., while some may be found in birds' nests. The most common European species is *T. sabulosus* (1).

Related to the Scarabaeidae are the beetles of the family Passalidae, distributed mostly in the tropics but with some species found as far as the Holarctic region. The illustrated species *Passalus interstitialis* (2) is native to Cuba. The female watches over the eggs as well as the larvae, which live in

decayed wood until they pupate, chasing
away even members of her own species.
The larvae have the third pair of legs
adapted to form a stridulatory organ
with which they produce a squeaking
noise.

95

Byrrhus pilula Linné, 1758

The pill beetle *B. pilula* is a 6.5—9.5 mm long beetle with an oval, very convex body, distributed throughout practically all Europe. It is found in thin, open woods from lowland to mountains and is most often found in clearings, woodland meadows, and in forest margins. It is very slow and like all pill beetles unable to fly (the wings are atrophied and the elytra fused). When disturbed it withdraws its tarsi into special grooves in its tibiae and the tibiae into grooves on the underside of the body. The antennae are also withdrawn into grooves on the underside of the prothorax when danger threatens and the beetle feigns death (thanatosis). It resembles a pebble or goat dropping and is able to remain in this pose for a relatively long time. All this, along with its sombre mimetic coloration, enables it to merge with its background when danger threatens and thus literally disappear from the enemy's sight. Adult beetles are phytophagous and in all probability feed on mosses, algae and lichens. The larva (1) is grub-like but strongly sclerotized with a strikingly large prothorax and terminal abdominal segment, which bears two protrusile appendages serving to facilitate the larva's movement or to hold it firmly inside the tunnel. The legs are relatively short. The larva lives in the upper soil layers, beneath stones or beneath a cushion of moss and is probably also phytophagous. It pupates in the ground in autumn. The adult beetle overwinters in the pupal chamber and emerges very early the following spring.

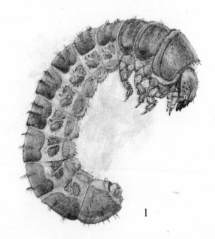

Some members of the Byrrhidae family belonging to the genus *Simplocaria* occur only above the upper forest limit in alpine meadows. They are usually coloured a lovely metallic golden-green. Because they live in isolated localities and are unable to fly they generally form endemic species in every large mountain range.

1

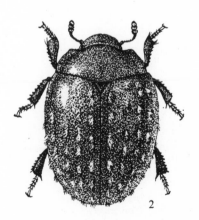

The closely related Nosodendridae family is represented in Europe by only a single species, *Nosodendron fasciculare* (2). It is similar to the pill beetles of the genus *Byrrhus*, but it does not have the grooves into which legs and antennae are drawn in *Byrrhus*, and the elytra are covered with tufts of rust-coloured hairs. It is found in old trees with continually escaping sap, into which it burrows completely out of sight. The larva, whose way of life is the same, resembles a miniature trilobite.

2

E. aenea, about 2 mm long, is a dark-coloured beetle with a conspicuous structure of the elytra and pronotum. It is widely distributed in central and northern Europe, including the UK, where it inhabits clear mountain streams and fast-flowing water. It is generally found under stones and on aquatic vegetation, to which it clings in the swift current with its strikingly long hooked claws. The beetles do not swim but only clamber slowly over submerged objects. A typical characteristic of the entire Elmidae family is its plastron respiration. The underside of the beetle's abdomen is covered with extremely fine, thick, hygroscopic hairs which continually carry an air supply, a layer of air trapped between the hairs, in which the concentration of oxygen is renewed by diffusion from the water. Opening into this layer of air are the stigmata of the tracheal system. Like all members of the family, *E. aenea* is phytophagous. The female attaches the eggs to aquatic vegetation, stones and various other submerged objects. The larva (1) is strongly sclerotized, flattened, and reminiscent of certain small woodlice. The larva's terminal abdominal segment bears three protrusile, branching, anal gills. The larva pupates on land, but in a very moist environment.

Many species of Elmidae are seriously endangered by the pollution of water. They are extremely sensitive to even small amounts of pollution; a slight change in the water's acidity is enough to disrupt the beetle's entire development.

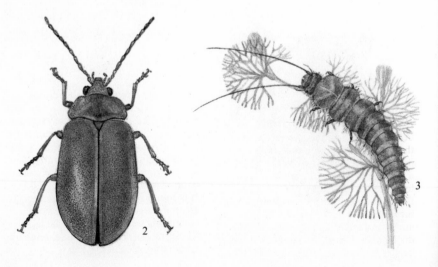

1

Closely related to the Dryopidae are the beetles of the Scirtidae family. One of the commonest members of this family in Europe is *Microcara testacea* (2). It is a phytophagous beetle, about 4—6 mm long, thickly covered with fine hairs, found in large numbers in damp meadows and in the vicinity of swamps and moorland. The larva (3) is readily distinguished from the larvae of other beetles by its long, multisegmented antennae. It breathes by means of protrusile anal gills and its development includes five instars. The larvae feed on detritus and sometimes may be observed crawling along on the underside of the surface film of stagnant water.

This species is one of the handsomest and most striking jewel beetles in Europe. It measures 9—18 mm and is distributed from Scandinavia to the Caucasus and from Spain through all Europe and western Siberia to the Altai. It is also found on all the islands of the Mediterranean, in Algeria and in Morocco. Its coloration is extremely variable. The yellow patches on the elytra, pronotum and underside of the body may merge, spread, or even disappear so that it would be hard to find two specimens with identical markings. The larva of this buprestid develops in various species of pine, mostly *Pinus silvestris* and *P. halepensis*. It may develop in the young stems of 6—7-year-old pines as well as in the trunks and thick branches of old trees and fresh tree stumps and may even be found frequently also in thick, partly exposed roots. Its development takes 2—4 years. The larva generally pupates during the month of June in a shallow pupal chamber in wood. The pupal development lasts 3—4 weeks. The adult beetle may be encountered from June to August on young pine shoots, where it feeds, or on the sun-warmed trunks, freshly felled logs or stumps of pine trees. *B. octoguttata* may be a problem in young pine stands, but generally it does not occur in such numbers as to be considered a real forest pest.

2

Buprestid larvae are creamy-white, very occasionally yellow or yellow-green, and apart from a few exceptions they develop in wood or in bark. They have a wide prothoracic segment, covering most of the head, and a long, cylindrical abdomen (1). On the underside of the broadened prothorax is a sclerotized longitudinal groove and on the upper side generally a double groove in the form of an inverted letter V or Y. Inside their burrows the larvae are always curved in the form of a letter U.

Buprestids also include among their number serious economic pests. The most serious of the lot are certain species of the genus *Sphenoptera*, e. g. *S. gossypii* (2) which is a serious pest of cotton plantations in Africa and tropical Asia.

1

This robust buprestid, measuring up to 35 mm, may be found in central Asia and in the easternmost parts of Europe. It inhabits semi-desert and steppe regions, dry pastureland and sunny banks. Unlike most buprestid larvae, which develop inside plant tissues, the larva of *J. variolaris* develops in the ground where it feeds on the roots of grasses, desert herbs and shrubs. It is adapted to life underground and shows very little resemblance to other buprestid larvae. It most closely resembles the larva of the longhorn beetle *Prionus coriarius.* The development of *J. variolaris* takes 2—3 years. The larva pupates in the ground in a firm cocoon made of sand cemented together with saliva. The adult beetles emerge early in spring, often in large numbers, whereupon they visit various herbs and shrubs whose foliage they eat. Often such a shrub looks like a decorated Christmas tree.

Buprestids of the genus *Julodis* are among the most attractive of all beetles. The range of some species extends from the deserts and semi-deserts of Africa and the Middle East even to southern Europe. The family's scientific name is composed of two Greek words: *bous,* meaning cattle, and *preto,* meaning I poison. Until recently it was believed that it was a case of mistaken identity — that it was not buprestids but poisonous Meloidae that had been eaten by grazing cattle. Recently, however, it was discovered that the bodies of certain Central American and North American buprestids contain a very effective alkaloid. It is therefore possible that the poisoning of cattle was truly caused by buprestids, perhaps precisely by species of the genus *Julodis,* which have always been and continue to be plentiful in the pasturelands of Greece.

Species of Trachyinae are atypical of buprestids. They are sometimes small and quite soberly coloured species such as *Trachys minuta,* one of the commonest European buprestids. It is only 3—3.5 mm long, triangular in shape and its development is different from that of most other buprestids. The female deposits the eggs on the sun-dappled leaves of goat willows, hazels or birches and the tiny larvae bore into the green leaf tissues inside which they develop. The development is relatively rapid (about 5—6 weeks) and during this time the larvae bore

characteristic mines called hyponomes
(1) in the leaves. The larva (2) is totally
unlike the larvae of other buprestids and
pupates directly in the mine. The adult
beetle emerges in late summer and
overwinters in the detritus at the base of
the food plant.

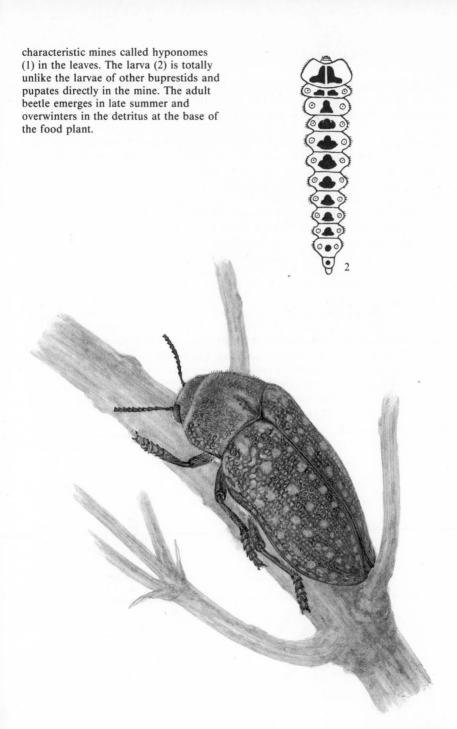

2

Anthaxia candens (PANZER, 1789)　　　　　　　　Buprestidae

A. candens is a relatively small (7—12 mm) but very colourful and striking buprestid. It is a central and southern European species with a range extending to western Europe in places. It is found in forest-steppe biotopes and its larvae develop beneath the bark on the trunk and thick branches of the Mahaleb Cherry (*Prunus mahaleb*), and less frequently on blackthorn and other cherry trees. The larval development takes 2—3 years and the larva pupates in late summer in a pupal chamber where wood and bark meet. The adult beetle emerges the same year but does not leave the pupal chamber, where it overwinters. During the first hot days in May the adult beetles fly out in large numbers. They are active during the warmest hours of the day, alighting on the leaves of the foodplant where they feed. Even though *A. candens* is sometimes quite plentiful in cherry orchards it does not cause serious damage to the trees, for the larva develops only in bruised, diseased or dying trunks and branches. Its body is flattened with a greatly widened front end which covers the entire head excepting the mouthparts. In its burrow the larva's body is curved in the form of a letter U. With the curved middle part of the body it compacts the fine particles of wood and excrement behind it. The larva is without legs and moves forward by extending and contracting the widened front part of the body, with the curved middle part serving as a support. Serving to hold it firmly in the burrow are four spherical processes on the hind end of the metathorax which are a typical feature of all larvae of the genus *Anthaxia*.

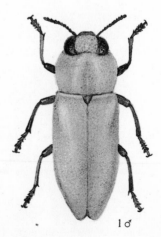

2 ♀　　　　　　　　　　　　　1 ♂

104

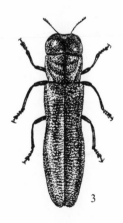

Forest-steppe and scrub biotopes, parks and gardens throughout practically all of Europe to southern Scandinavia are inhabited by *A. nitidula.* Its larva develops under the bark of dying branches of practically all fruit trees. This species exhibits marked sexual dimorphism: the male (1) is a metallic gold-green whereas the female (2) has the head and pronotum coloured orange and the elytra metallic blue-green.

Paracylindromorphus subuliformis (3), a common beetle of all southern European steppes, is a representative of a group of buprestids that reside exclusively in steppes and whose larvae develop inside the stems of grasses. The body of these buprestids is longish-cylindrical, adapted for life inside grass stems.

3

105

Ampedus sanguinolentus (SCHRANK, 1789)   Elateridae

A. sanguinolentus, a 9—12 mm long beetle with striking red and black coloration, is distributed throughout all Europe and Siberia. It can usually be distinguished from the other red and black species of *Ampedus* by the black oval patches on the elytra; these, however, may very occasionally be absent. *A. sanguinolentus* inhabits forests from lowland districts to fairly high up in the mountains, but it prefers flood-plain forests where it is always very plentiful. Its larva, coloured rusty-yellow and strongly sclerotized with a pointed terminal abdominal segment, slightly resembles a mealworm. Click beetle larvae of this type are called wireworms because they truly resemble a piece of rusty, curved wire. The eggs are deposited singly in the bark of old, decaying stumps and trunks of broad-leaved trees, occasionally also conifers. The larva develops between the wood and dead bark or in the surface layers of rotting wood. It is predacious and its development takes 2—3 years. As in all wireworms the number of larval instars varies and may be anything from 9 to 15. The larva pupates in summer in a small pupal chamber close to the surface and the adult beetle emerges as early as late summer. However it overwinters in the pupal chamber and does not climb out until the following spring. Adult beetles can be found on the leaves of forest vegetation, on old tree stumps and on the flowers of umbelliferous plants.

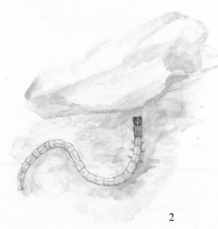

2

Click beetle larvae (wireworms) are generally fairly uniform, coloured a rusty hue or brown, very occasionally black, circular in cross-section and with a pointed terminal abdominal segment. The larvae of some click beetles, however, are greatly flattened with spade-like, strongly sclerotized head and complex, sclerotized appendages (urogomphi) on the terminal abdominal segment. This type is adapted for digging in hard, heavy soil; the larva of *Agrypnus murina* (1) is an example. Quite different from the usual type of wireworm are the larvae of the genus *Cardiophorus* (2), which are a pale

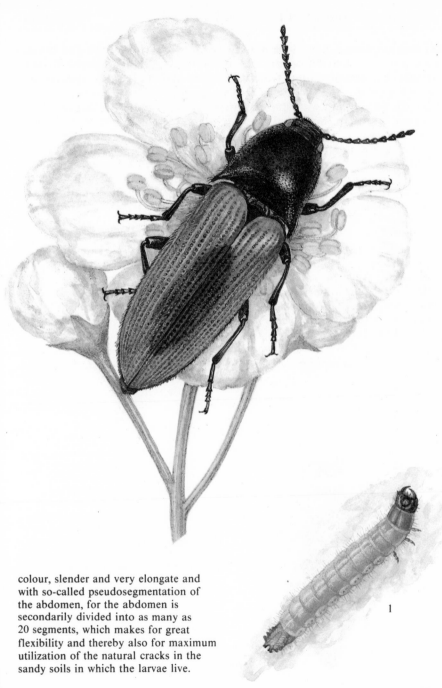

colour, slender and very elongate and
with so-called pseudosegmentation of
the abdomen, for the abdomen is
secondarily divided into as many as
20 segments, which makes for great
flexibility and thereby also for maximum
utilization of the natural cracks in the
sandy soils in which the larvae live.

1

107

Ctenicera virens (SCHRANK, 1781)   Elateridae

C. virens is a slender, strikingly coloured beetle measuring up to
20 mm in length. The elytra are rusty-yellow, the head and pronotum
metallic green or violet. Near the tip of each elytron is a longitudinal
patch of the same colour as the head and pronotum; very occasionally it may be absent. The antennae are widened from the third segment onwards; the female's ones are serrate, the male's conspicuously pectinate. C. virens is distributed throughout central and northern Europe and in North America. It is found primarily in foothill
and mountain forests, mostly in the forest margins, in clearings and in
woodland meadows. In eentral Europe it occurs up to the upper limit
of the forest. The larva is up to 30 mm long, black-brown above and
rust-coloured beneath. The strongly sclerotized head bears a large
pointed spine in the centre of the forehead. The larva's mandibles are
short and crescent-shaped. The larva is mostly phytophagous, though
occasionally it devours the larva or pupa of some other insect. Its abdominal segments are increasingly larger towards the hind end and
a pale dorsal line runs down the entire length of the abdomen. The
terminal abdominal segment is strongly sclerotized and bears greatly
branched urogomphi, which the larva presses against the roof of the
tunnel as props when burrowing through the surface layers of the
soil. The fleshy process on the underside of the terminal segment,
known as the pygopod, serves the same purpose. The larva takes 3—4
years to develop and pupates in spring. The adult beetle emerges
in early summer and visits meadow vegetation and very occasionally
flowers.

1 ♂

The male of the species *Ctenicera
pectinicornis* (1) has conspicuously
pectinate antennae. In central and
northern Europe it is one of the
commonest mountain and submontane
click beetle species and may often be
encountered even above the upper forest
limit in alpine meadows.

Apart from a few exceptions all
members of the Elateridae family
possess the power of leaping from
a resting position to a height of several
tens of centimetres accompanied by
a clicking sound. On the hind edge of
the prothorax (between the anterior
coxae) there is a long narrow process
extending rearward which in a certain

108

position fits snugly into a notch on the mesothorax (2). Sudden contraction of the muscles forces this process into the respective notch and the kick-back flings the beetle upward.

D. linearis belongs to a small group of click beetles (subfamilies Denticollinae and Diminae) which do not possess the typical power of leaping and clicking and have small, humped pronotum narrower than the elytra. It is a 9—13 mm long, slender, conspicuously grooved beetle with an almost cylindrical, uneven pronotum. The males are usually darker than the females and as a rule also conspicuously smaller. This click beetle inhabits practically the whole of Europe including all of Scandinavia, Siberia and Japan. It is definitely a woodland species and found in all types of forests from lowland to high mountain districts. The eggs are laid singly in spring under the bark of dead trees, tree stumps or branches. The larva is important as a major insect predator. It feeds on all insects and insect larvae occurring under bark as well as snails, eearthworms and even small amphibians hidden under bark (usually hibernating there). During its 2—3-year development, the larva undergoes 10 to 14 instars. It is black above, grey-black below and very strongly sclerotized. The terminal abdominal segment bears robust, branched urogomphi. In general appearance the larva is slightly reminiscent of the younger larvae of ground beetles of the genus *Carabus*. It pupates in spring in a shallow pupal chamber under bark or in the outermost layers of wood, very occasionally also in the ground at the foot of the tree stump or tree trunk in which its development took place. The pupal stage lasts 2—3 weeks. Adult beetles alight on woodland vegetation, on bark, and also on flowering umbelliferous plants.

2

The few members of the subfamily Diminae, e.g. *Dima elateroides* (1), are short, plump click beetles that have secondarily lost the ability to fly. Three species of this subfamily are found also in southern Europe, where they occur in the montane to alpine zone of all larger mountain ranges. The larvae are phytophagous and live in the ground, the adult beetles are most often found under stones.

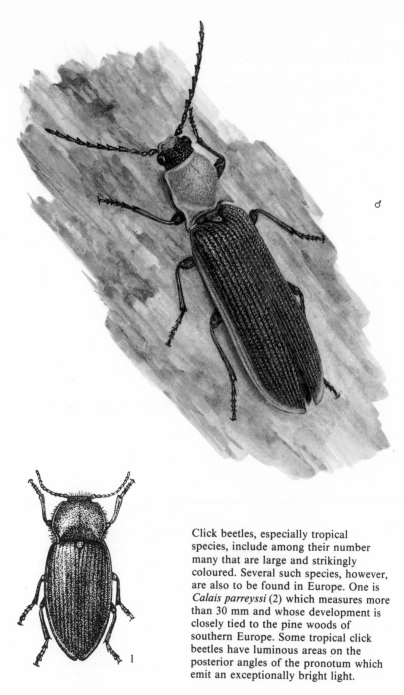

♂

Click beetles, especially tropical species, include among their number many that are large and strikingly coloured. Several such species, however, are also to be found in Europe. One is *Calais parreyssi* (2) which measures more than 30 mm and whose development is closely tied to the pine woods of southern Europe. Some tropical click beetles have luminous areas on the posterior angles of the pronotum which emit an exceptionally bright light.

111

Common Glow-worm
Lampyris noctiluca (LINNÉ, 1758)   Lampyridae

The Common Glow-worm occurs everywhere throughout Europe in damp localities generally overgrown with thick vegetation from lowland districts to high up in the mountains. The male is 10—12 mm long, the female 15—20 mm long. It is a beetle soberly coloured black-brown with marked differences between the sexes. The female is wingless and resembles a larva; the male has wings. A typical feature of all members of this family is the arching, forward-protracted pronotum which completely covers the opisthognathous head from above. All glow-worms possess the power of bioluminescence, i.e. the emission of cold light. This is a very complex process during which light is emitted when a chemical substance, luciferin, is oxidized by free oxygen in the presence of an enzyme, luciferase. Photogenic organs are located on either side of the last abdominal segments and are present also in the larvae and pupae, and even in the eggs. They are apparently governed by neurohormones for they can be 'turned of' or 'turned on' as required. Whereas the adult beetle does not feed, the larvae of the common glow-worm are predacious and feed on snails. Their body is elongated, slightly narrowed at both ends, and the small head (1) is furnished with sharp mandibles which have an internal duct. Via this duct the larva injects into the body of its victim a poisonous substance secreted by paired glands in the anterior gut which also breaks down proteins and thus provides preliminary digestion. The liquefied contents are then sucked up by the larva with its maxillae and labrum. The larva moults five times and pupates in spring. The pupal stage lasts two weeks.

1

The light signals of glow-worms serve as a means of communication between members of the species and to assist in the attraction of the sexes for mating. In tropical forests, where many species of glow-worms occur in a single biotope, each species has developed special light signals. The various species emit light of different wavelengths or else at regular intervals specific for the given species.

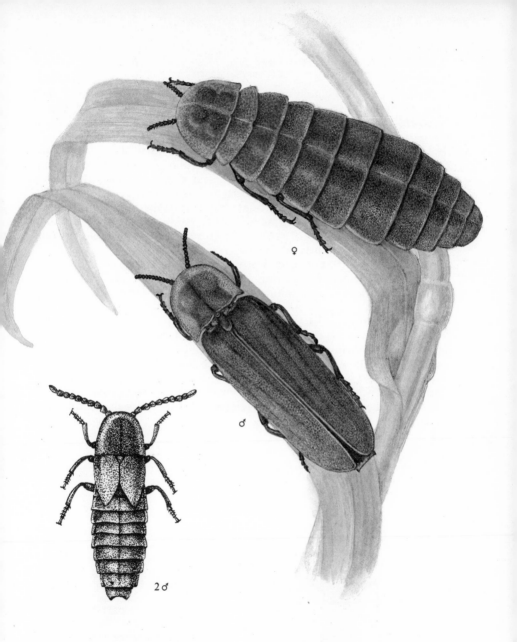

♀

♂

2♂

Such a nocturnal whirl of glow-worms is an unforgettable sight, for the darkness is filled with the flashing lights of hundreds of beetles — lights of varying intensity and colour emitted at varying intervals. Only the males fly, however, even though the females of some species also possess wings. The males of the warmth-loving, rather rare European species *Phosphaneus hemipterus* (2) have greatly abbreviated elytra and slightly resemble rove beetles.

C. fusca is one of the commonest European beetles, appearing in very large numbers in spring. It is 11—15 mm long with a flattened, slightly sclerotized body coloured a dark hue but with the posterior half of the pronotum and antennae coloured orange. Because the entire body is only faintly sclerotized (as in all other members of the Cantharidae family), *C. fusca* is soft, this being particularly conspicuous in the elytra. It is widely distributed throughout central and northern Europe where it inhabits open woods, forest-steppes, and overgrown banks and gardens; it is also found high up in the mountains. Adult beetles are predacious, but traces of their feeding were observed also on the fresh new shoots of coniferous trees. The eggs are laid in summer in the upper soil layers. The newly-hatched larvae have atrophied mouth parts and do not feed. Within 4—6 days, after having moulted once or twice, they change into active predacious larvae without appendages on the last abdominal segment (1), which moult again some 6—7 times. The larvae are dark brown with black, practically geometric markings on the thorax and abdomen and their body is completely covered with fine, very short and thick hairs. They live on the surface of the ground or in the upper layers of soil and are extremely predacious. Via a channel on the inner side of the mandibles they inject digestive juices into their prey thereby enabling extra-oral digestion (outside the body). The larvae hibernate and pupate the following spring in the ground; development thus takes one year.

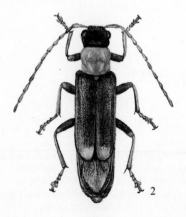

2

The Cantharidae family also includes two large genera of small inconspicuous beetles: *Malthinus* and *Malthodes*. They are tiny, only 3—4 mm long, with slender, very soft bodies and may be encountered practically everywhere from lowland to high mountain districts. They are generally found in meadows, forest clearings and heaths but may also be seen in steppes and forest-steppes. The two very similar and related genera are represented in Europe by some 50 species that can be distinguished only with extreme difficulty. One of the commonest is *Malthodes minimus* (2),

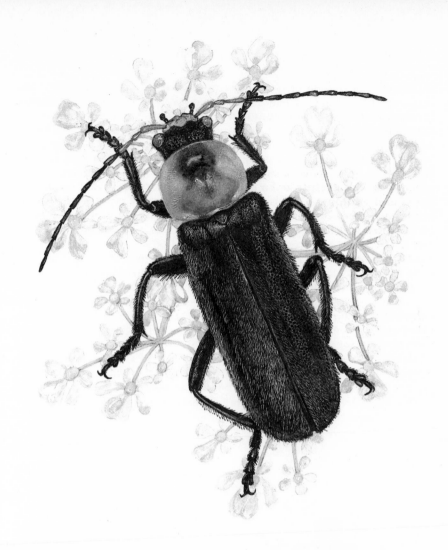

1

found throughout all Europe excepting
the Alps and Balkans. The Cantharidae
and the preceding Lampyridae family
belong, along with several other smaller
families, to the group Cantharoidea
whose members are distinguished by
having the body only faintly sclerotized
and of relatively uniform shape,
a so-called cantharid-type body.

115

Europe is the home of only eight species of the predominantly tropical Lycidae family. The largest and most striking is *Dictyoptera aurora*, distributed throughout all central and northern Europe including the UK. It is an 8—13 mm long, flattened beetle coloured bright red with a conspicuous structure of the pronotum and longitudinally ribbed elytra that are furthermore patterned with a distinct network of square depressions. The head is small and partly concealed beneath the front edge of the pronotum. *D. aurora* is a typical inhabitant of deep forests, particularly in foothill and mountain districts. The adult beetles as well as the larvae are predacious and prey on other insects. The eggs are laid in decayed wood and under the bark of old, dying trees or tree stumps. The larvae are flattened and slightly reminiscent of glow-worm larvae. Unlike the latter (and unlike cantharid larvae), all Lycidae larvae are glabrous. They feed on xylophagous insects.

To date relatively little is known about the life history of Lycidae beetles. The larvae of some species, e.g. the common European species *Lygistropterus sanguineus* (1), have the ninth abdominal segment coloured bright orange and furnished with large black urogomphi. The tropical regions of the Old and New World are the home of hundreds of very striking species with conspicuous warning coloration which are poisonous. As a matter of interest their body shape and coloration are mimicked by numerous other, harmless beetles, especially members of the Cerambycidae family.

1

The group Cantharoidea is represented in Europe by yet another, small but bionomically very interesting family, namely the Drilidae family, which has only two species in Europe. The most plentiful is *Drilus flavescens,* found in the dry and warm, generally steppe localities of Europe. This is the only species of *Drilus* in Britain. The males and females differ markedly, in the same way as the glow-worms. The male (2) has long, pectinate antennae and fully developed elytra as well as the second pair of wings; the female (3) is completely wingless with short widened

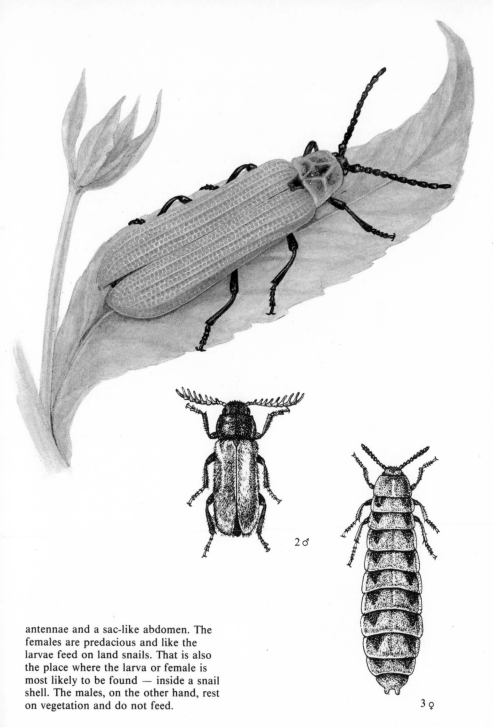

antennae and a sac-like abdomen. The
females are predacious and like the
larvae feed on land snails. That is also
the place where the larva or female is
most likely to be found — inside a snail
shell. The males, on the other hand, rest
on vegetation and do not feed.

2 ♂

3 ♀

Larder Beetle
Dermestes lardarius LINNÉ, 1758 Dermestidae

The Larder Beetle is a common household pest. This relatively incon-spicuous beetle, measuring 7—9 mm, today has a cosmopolitan dis-tribution but apparently originated in Eurasia. The fertilized female always lays the eggs directly on the material the larva feeds on (or-ganic remains of animal origin) but only after she has consumed food rich in protein. The eggs are laid in batches of 6—8 over a period of about three months (in Europe from June until August). At the opti-mum temperature of 18—20 °C the larva hatches within 7—8 days; it is pale at first but after a few hours turns a darker colour. The larva of the Larder Beetle is a polypod (eruciform) larva, thickly covered with long hairs and furnished with spiny urogomphi (1). Its development includes 5—7 larval instars. The fully grown larva of the last instar abandons the food in which it developed and bores itself a tunnel in the nearest suitable material, which may be soil as well as paper, wood, or even a lead pipe. The entire development from egg to adult beetle takes 2—3 months under ideal temperature conditions. In heated premises or in warm districts there may even be several gen-erations in one year. It is always the adult beetle that overwinters. The Larder Beetle causes greatest damage to animal products: hides, stored smoked meats, woollen fabrics, stuffed animals, etc. Eradicat-ing this pest is extremely difficult for contact chemical insecticides do not penetrate to the larva's skin because of its thick coat of long hairs.

1

Another pest of the Dermestidae family is *Attagenus pellio* (2). It is not as widespread as the Larder Beetle but the range of foods the larva eats is far greater and by no means limited to animal products. It includes also materials of vegetable origin such as carpets, upholstered furniture, cereal grains, flour, sugar, granulated mixtures, rolled oats and botanical collections. The adult beetle (as in all species of *Attagenus)* feeds mainly on hawthorn, blackthorn and spiraea but will eat the pollen of a wide variety of plants. There

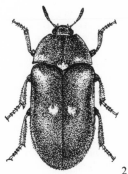

2

are as many as 11 larval instars and larval development may take as long as three years, if conditions are unfavourable. Generally, however, development takes one year and the adult beetle overwinters.

Museum Beetle
Anthrenus museorum (LINNÉ, 1761) Dermestidae

This, some 3 mm long beetle is one of the most notorious pests of museum collections, not only of insect collections, but also of skins of mammals etc. Its larvae, however, also attack other materials of animal origin, e.g. hides and furs, wigs, woollen and silk fabrics, smoked meats, cheeses and even glues. They have likewise been known to damage linen and cotton fabrics as well as products made from flour. The Museum Beetle occasionally occurs also in stores of cereals, but there the larvae apparently feed on the remains of other insects. The adult beetles feed on pollen, e.g. on flowering hawthorn and on various umbelliferous plants. Flowers are also the place where males and females copulate. The fertilized females then fly into households, warehouses and other places where they might find food for the larvae. They lay 20—30 eggs and the entire development takes 7—14 months, depending on the temperature and on the quantity and quality of available food. It is always the larva that overwinters. It is short, robust and thickly covered with long hairs. There are 9—11 larval instars. The pupa generally remains inside the exuvia of the last larval instar. In the wild the larvae are often found in birds' nests as well as in the webs of larger spiders where they feed on the remains of insects. Frequently the larva also develops inside the cocoons of various moths. Museum collections that are not properly cared for may be completely destroyed within a short time. In museums this pest may be kept at bay, for example, by gassing with various chemical agents, heating above 32 °C or simply by cooling to a temperature of 4 °C.

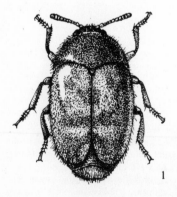

The Dermestidae family includes another important pest of stored grain products, namely the Khapra Beetle (*Trogoderma granarium*) (1) about 2—3 mm long and coloured a rusty hue, which spread with shipments of grain products from Malaysia, India and Ceylon to practically all parts of the world. Unlike other pests of the Dermestidae family this species shows a predilection for materials of vegetable origin, flour, and flour products, but has also been known to do damage to dried milk and blood.

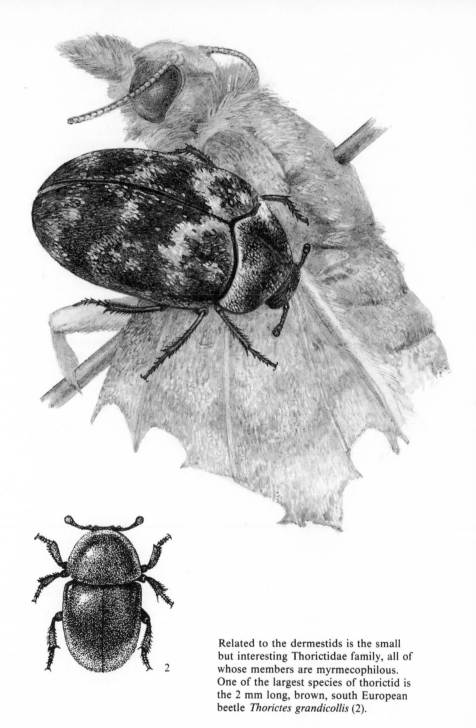

Related to the dermestids is the small but interesting Thorictidae family, all of whose members are myrmecophilous. One of the largest species of thorictid is the 2 mm long, brown, south European beetle *Thorictes grandicollis* (2).

This beetle measures 4.5—6 mm, is almost black and has a small head hidden by the forward edge of the pronotum. Like most anobiids it is found in old, dead and dry wood. During the mating season, i.e. in spring, the males knock their head and pronotum on the walls of their burrows to attract a mate. The knocking is amplified by the dry wood and makes a distinctive ticking sound. The eggs are laid directly on dry, dead wood which the larva is able to digest with the aid of symbiotic bacteria that break down the cellulose. These bacteria are transferred from the female's alimentary canal to the eggs when they are laid and the newly emerged larvae eat them as they bite through the eggshell. The larva is white, soft and grub-like and its development usually takes one year, during which it moults four times. Infested dry, dead wood is literally changed to powder by generations of the larvae of wood-boring beetles and in the end falls apart completely. There have even been instances when entire wooden buildings have collapsed because the supporting beams were destroyed by beetles. If the wood is not heavily infested it is possible to inject various insecticides into the flying holes with a syringe. Smaller and valuable objects are gassed with cyanide in special containers. Applying a preventive coat of an effective substance to rafters also helps. The best remedy, however, is to burn the infested object.

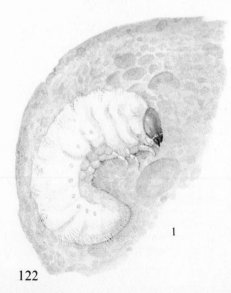

1

Anobiids also include a number of species that do not develop in wood. One, for instance, is the Bread Beetle (*Stegobium paniceum*) whose larva (1) develops in food products and is a serious stored products pest. It infests mainly products made with flour but also chocolate, cocoa, smoked meats, dried herbs and spices and even other foodstuffs. Somewhat peculiar is the predilection of another species — *Lasioderma serricorne* (2) which feeds on dry tobacco leaves and tobacco products. Originally native to Central

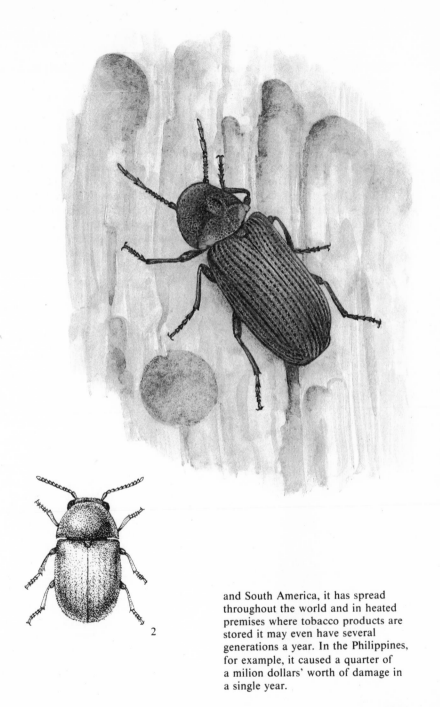

2

and South America, it has spread throughout the world and in heated premises where tobacco products are stored it may even have several generations a year. In the Philippines, for example, it caused a quarter of a milion dollars' worth of damage in a single year.

Hedobia imperialis (LINNÉ, 1767)   Anobiidae

The Anobiidae family includes a great many species that do not cause any damage. *H. imperialis* is one example. It is a beetle about 5 mm long with whitish-grey, relatively complex markings on the brown elytra. As in all anobiids the front edge of the pronotum extends forward but does not conceal the entire head as in many other species. *H. imperialis* is distributed throughout practically all Europe including the UK, being particularly abundant in the southern parts of the continent. It is found in forest-steppes and open, sun-dappled broad-leaved, mostly oak, forests. The larva of this species, like that of all anobiids, is grub-like, only slightly sclerotized and coloured white. It occurs in the wood of dead but as yet hard branches, of oaks and hornbeams, but also in elms, lime trees and fruit trees. Larval development takes one year and the adult beetles can be seen already in early spring. Like all anobiids they crawl about slowly and hesitantly and on warm evenings they often fly up in the air. Greater numbers of these beetles may be found on flowering hawthorn. *H. imperialis* generally inhabits only original biotopes undisturbed by man and may thus serve as an indicator of an unspoiled biotope in the same way as the related species *H. regalis* and *H. pubescens.*

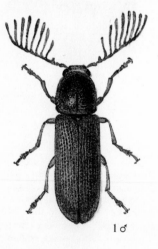

1 ♂

The anobiid found in greatest numbers in the wild is without doubt the species *Ptilinus pectinicornis* (1). About 5 mm long, it is a slender, cylindrical beetle with marked differences between the sexes. The female has long, simple antennae, whereas the male's are conspicuously pectinate from the fourth segment onward. This anobiid is distributed throughout practically all Europe where it inhabits dead trees that are still standing, mainly beech and willow, in which it bores thousands of minute, round holes from which powdered wood dribbles. Such trees are conspicuous from afar for they look as if they were sprinkled with a yellowish powder. In houses it can damage wooden furniture.

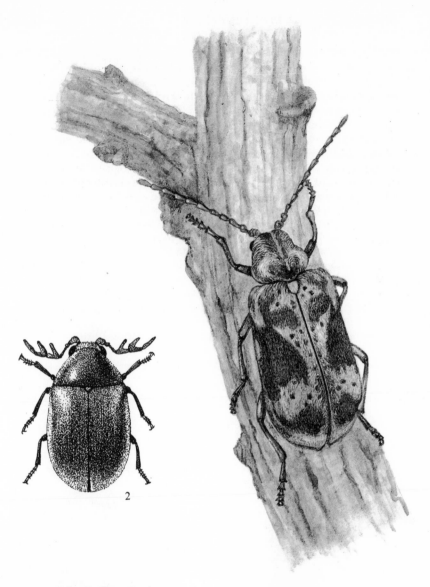

The separate subfamily Dorcatominae
comprises short and robust anobiids
with greatly enlarged terminal antennal
segments, for example *Dorcatoma
dresdenensis* (2), common in central
Europe, which lives on dead bracket
fungi.

B. capucinus is a robust, cylindrical beetle with brick-red elytra and head and the pronotum coloured black. It exhibits marked variability in size (6—15 mm). Its range includes all central and southern Europe, north Africa and Asia Minor. It is readily distinguished from the other members of the family by its typical coloration, for other bostrychid beetles are generally black or brown. The pronotum of this species is nearly spherical and conceals the small hypognathous head. The larva develops in the dead but as yet hard wood of broad-leaved trees, chiefly oaks, hornbeams, walnut and fruit trees, primarily in steppe and forest-steppe regions but also in flood-plain forests. The larvae are capable of transforming a dead branch into a hollow tube filled with powdered wood for one such branch may be inhabited by many successive generations. The larvae are grub-like and only slightly sclerotized and differ from anobiid larvae by having a small, reduced head and a narrower thorax. Larval development may take several years, depending on the quality and quantity of the available food, which also influences the size of the adult beetle. If the larvae develop in wood that is already beginning to decay and provides little nourishment or if they have insufficient food then the resulting beetles are small — so-called 'hungry forms'.

A serious warehouse pest of the Bostrychidae family is the species *Rhizoperta dominica* which has a cosmopolitan distribution. Its larva develops in foodstuffs of vegetable origin.

2

Tropical and desert regions are the home of numerous species of Bostrychidae that have an interestingly formed pronotum or elytra. One example is *Bostrychoplites cornutus* (1) of the Sahara Desert which was introduced to central Europe in shipments of timber. On the forward edge of the pronotum it has two long, curved horns which are covered with numerous sharp granules. In other species the elytra are truncated and bear various spines and horns. Relatively plentiful in central and eastern Europe is the species *Psoa*

vienensis (2), whose larvae develop in the dead stems and branches of the grape vine. It is frequently said to be a pest of grape vines but this is probably based on incorrect data for the larvae truly live only in the dead parts of the plant.

This inconspicuous, rusty-brown beetle, measuring about 3—4.5 mm, is more often encountered in households than in the wild, even though it is distributed throughout the whole Holarctic region. It is found mainly in old broad-leaved trees with dry crumbling wood in warm districts at lower elevations, less often in hilly country. In the wild its way of life is much like that of anobiids and its larva (1) also greatly resembles the larvae of anobiids, being white, grub-like, and only slightly sclerotized; it differs from the latter in that it does not have small spines on the abdominal segments. Larval development in the wild takes one year and the adult beetles may be seen already early in spring. The male's body is slender, nearly cylindrical and a uniform rusty colour, whereas the female's is very convex, as if inflated, and coloured brown with a pale transverse bar on the elytra. In both sexes the head is partly concealed by the front edge of the pronotum.

This species, however, is encountered far more frequently in households and in places where foodstuffs are stored. There the larva develops in all kinds of dry foodstuffs, ranging from products made of flour to dry smoked meats. Any dry matter of organic origin suffices for its developmental needs: old fabrics, paper, cork linoleum, felt watermain insulation, old rafters, and even panels in the production of which use was made of fine wood shavings, sawdust or chaff. In heated buildings *P. fur* may have two generations a year and often occurs even during the winter months, particularly during a spell of mild weather.

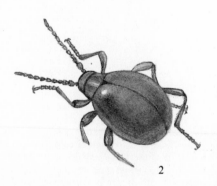

2

Features that distinguish all members of the Ptinidae family are greatly widened elytra that look as if they were inflated and generally also reduced wings. The first trait, inflated elytra, is most pronounced in *Gibbium psylloides* (2). This is a cosmopolitan species and it is not clear which geographic region is its place of origin. It is a frequent pest in European households. Other synanthropic Ptinidae also occur in houses, often in plague numbers. In such a case they generally terrify the people living there.

1

However such a mass occurrence usually ends as quickly as it came and as a rule it is thus unnecessary to use chemical agents to get rid of these beetles.

In the wild *T. mauritanicus*, measuring 6—11 mm, occurs under the bark of dying trees and tree stumps and in rotting wood, where it feeds on other insects and their larvae. It is found everywhere in warm lowland districts and hilly country. The larva is elongated, white, only slightly sclerotized with just the head, prothorax and terminal abdominal segment strongly sclerotized (1). The terminal abdominal segment furthermore bears a pair of sharp, spiny urogomphi. The larva is also very predacious and feeds on xylophagous insects and their larvae. During its year-long development it moults 3—4 times. This species has likewise adapted to life in man's dwellings and warehouses, though not nearly to such a degree as the Anobiidae, Ptinidae and Dermestidae. It is often reported to be a pest of stored cereals, flour and products made from flour. In warehouses, however, only the adult beetles are pests; the larvae are predacious and rid stored foodstuffs of other harmful insects, in warehouses as well as households. On several occasions the larva was observed attacking and avidly consuming the larvae of dermestid beetles of the genera *Dermestes, Attagenus* and *Anthrenus*. Several closely related species of the genus *Tenebrioides* have been observed to date only in the wild, where their way of life is like that of natural populations of *T. mauritanicus*. The question is why, of the many related species, only this single one has partially adapted to life in man's dwellings.

3

1

The Trogossitidae are distributed predominantly in the tropical regions of South America; only a few members are also found in Europe. They are usually oval, greatly flattened beetles and their development takes place in rotten or mouldy wood. The largest Palaearctic representative of this family is *Peltis grossum* (2), found on fir trees in all

mountain districts of Europe and
Siberia. Its flying holes look like coin
slots. An exception to the general 'body
structure' typical of this family is the
relatively common European species
Nemosoma elongatum (3) which has
a very long and slender, nearly
cylindrical body adapted for
a predacious way of life in the burrows
of other xylophagous insects, chiefly
Scolytidae.

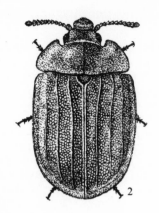

2

Thanasimus formicarius (LINNÉ, 1758)   Cleridae

T. formicarius is one of the many beneficial beetles. This red, black and white, 7—10 mm long beetle is distributed throughout Europe, in Africa and in Siberia. It is the only member of the entire warmth-loving family Cleridae that succeded in adapting to the harsh climate of northern Europe. It is found everywhere, from lowland to mountain districts, but is much less common at lower elevations than in the mountains. It is predacious and agile, hunting various kinds of insects that are often far bigger than itself. The larva (1) is pink and little sclerotized, only the head and last abdominal segment, which bears paired urogomphi, are strongly sclerotized and coloured brown. One of the greatest predators among beetle larvae, it lives under the bark of trees, mostly conifers, where it preys on the larvae of other insects, mainly bark beetles (Scolytidae). Through T. formicarius is a very plentiful species even under normal conditions, in years when bark beetles reach plague numbers it, too, registers a population explosion. In such years T. formicarius and its larvae, along with adult snake flies (Raphidioptera), are among the most important eradicators of bark beetles and their larvae. For this reason it was introduced into the United States and Canada to help control bark beetles outbreaks.

2

The Cleridae is mostly a tropical family with only a few species occurring in Europe. These are all predacious beetles whose larvae live under bark or in wood in the burrows of other insects that they hunt. One of the few exceptions is the small, metallic blue-green *Necrobia violacea* (2), which has a worldwide distribution. The larvae of this species, as well as the larvae of other beetles of the genus *Necrobia*, do not live under bark or in wood but on carrion, where they prey chiefly on the larvae of flies. The typical colour of all *Necrobia*

1

species is a metallic blue;
furthermore some have legs and
sometimes also the pronotum and base
of the elytra coloured a rusty hue. They
are small (5 mm long at the most), very
quick beetles that often occur in great
numbers on large carcasses.

133

Trichodes apiarius (Linné, 1758)   Cleridae

T. apiarius is one of the most striking European beetles that visit flowers. It is a 10—15 mm long beetle, brightly coloured with red and blue transverse bands and with a long, relatively thick coat of hairs. It is distributed throughout central and southern Europe and in north Africa. It is fond of warm, sunny biotopes, mostly steppe and forest-steppe hillsides, but also makes its way via valleys relatively high up into mountain districts. Adult beetles often visit the flowers of various, mostly umbelliferous, plants, but also crowfoot, hawkweed, etc. However they do not feed on the pollen of these plants but lie there in wait for other insects which they overpower by a fierce onslaught, for T. apiarius, like all other members of this family, is predacious. Its development, however, differs somewhat from that of other Cleridae, for its larvae do not live in wood and do not prey on the larvae of other insects but live in the nests of solitary and social bees. The larva is elongated, up to 2 cm long, pink, and covered with long, erect hairs. Only the head and last abdominal segment with urogomphi are more strongly sclerotized and dark in colour. In the nests of wild bees as well as in the hives of honey-bees they feed on the bee larvae. Inasmuch as this species is not particularly plentiful the damage it causes in beehives is not great and is definitely offset in sufficient measure by the beneficial activity of the adult beetles.

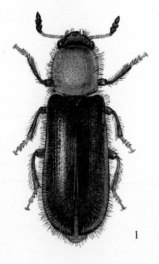

1

One of the rare European species of the family Cleridae is *Dermestoides sanguinicollis* (1), found in the warmest forest-steppe regions and flood-plain forests of central and southern Europe. Its larva lives in the trunks of old, dying oaks, where it feeds on the larvae of xylophagous insects, mostly longhorn beetles, buprestids, and bark-boring beetles. A peculiar clerid with abbreviated elytra is the species *Emmepus elegans* (2) found in central Asia with its range extending into the easternmost parts of Europe. Its larvae live inside old reed stems where they feed on the larvae of other insects, mostly buprestids of the genus *Paracylindromorphus*.

2

Malachius bipustulatus (LINNÉ, 1758)   Malachiidae

M. bipustulatus is commonly found on a wide variety of flowering plants from spring until late summer. This 5.5—6 mm long beetle, coloured metallic green with small red patches on the pronotum and elytra, is distributed throughout Europe from lowland districts to relatively high up in the mountains. The adult beetles are predacious and feed on small insects that visit blossoms: aphids, small flies, etc. Copulation takes place in spring and the female lays 10—30 eggs in cracks in the bark. The pink, faintly sclerotized and very agile larvae (1) hatch after about 12 days; only the head and last abdominal segment with urogomphi are more strongly sclerotized and a darker hue. The larva is predacious and feeds on the larvae and pupae of small xylophagous insects. During its development it probably undergoes only three larval instars.

The males of all members of the subfamily Malachiinae are furnished with interesting organs called excitatoria, which immediately before and during copulation secrete substances that attract the female and stimulate mating. They are located on widely varied parts of the body: on the head, antennae, tibiae, abdomen or elytra. In the species *M. bipustulatus* these excitatory organs are located on the forehead between the antennae in a depression with stiff, outspread hairs that help disperse the scent of the secreted substances. In other species these excitatory organs are much more complex.

2

Species of the subfamily Malachiinae are characterized by another interesting feature. When danger threatens or when irritated by direct contact these beetles protrude special vescicles on the sides of the pronotum and abdomen which fill with orange haemolymph and serve to frighten off the enemy. In addition the beetles are evidently poisonous or at least unpalatable to various predators.

Examples of the related family Melyridae, that are very common in Europe, include *Dolichosoma lineare* (2) and *Dasytes plumbeus* (3) of the subfamily Dasytinae. The first, conspicuously elongated and slender beetle, is found primarily in forest-steppe regions, the second from lowland to mountain districts.

1

3

137

H. dermestoides is distributed throughout Europe, occurring mostly in hilly country and mountain districts, mainly at elevations where pure beech and beech mixed with fir grow. Whereas the female is rust-coloured and exhibits only slight variability, the male is extremely variable both in size (6—18 mm) and coloration, which may be entirely black, entirely rusty, beige, or a combination of all these hues. The maxillary palps in the male have a secondarily increased number of segments and are thickened and conspicuously fan-shaped (flabellate). The eggs are laid in cracks in dead trees (mainly beech). The larva of the first instar, which is about 2 mm long with a large head, five simple eyes (stemmata) and truncated last abdominal segment, burrows into wood. The larvae of the ensuing instars are markedly different morphologically (1), resembling more the larvae of sawflies (Tenthredinidae) than the larva of a beetle. They are long, cylindrical, faintly sclerotized, with a teardrop-shaped prothorax, a long, spiny process on the last abdominal segment, relatively long legs, and with no stemmata. The larvae bore horizontal tunnels in wood, pushing the fine sawdust out with their legs and with the aid of the spiny abdominal process. A tree that has been attacked by these larvae looks as if it were dusted with white flour. Development takes one year. The larvae pupate early in spring and the adult beetles emerge very early the following spring, usually in large numbers. They do not feed and as a rule live only a few days.

The larva of *H. dermestoides* does not feed on the wood in which it lives but on ambrosia fungi of the species *Endomyces hylecoeti* that grow on the walls of the tunnels made by the larvae. When the eggs are laid the female dusts them with the spores of the fungus which the first larval instars then carry with them into the tunnels in the wood.

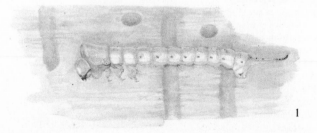

1

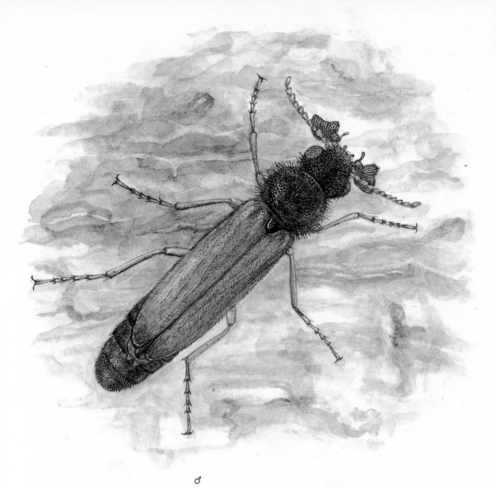

♂

Another European species belonging
to this family is *Lymexylon navale* (2). It
is much rarer, definitely warmth-loving,
and can be readily identified by the
pronotum, which is several times as long
as it is wide. The larvae of this species
live only in the hard wood of oaks
which they reduce with their tunnels.
In the tropics there are even some
species of Lymexylidae that have greatly
shortened elytra and live together with
termites.

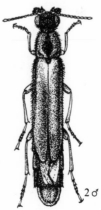

2 ♂

139

G. quadripunctatus is the largest European representative of the Nitidulidae family. It is 4—6.5 mm long with a slightly convex body and four conspicuous orange patches on the elytra. It is distributed throughout Europe (in the south only in mountains); in Siberia its range extends to the Far East, where it forms a different subspecies. This species is a typical inhabitant of mountain and submontane regions, mainly beech and spruce forests. It is most frequently found on the oozing and fermenting sap of bruised trees where its habits are saprophagous, but sometimes also predacious. The larva is flattened and broad with very short legs and a more strongly sclerotized terminal abdominal segment, which bears relatively long, branched urogomphi. In this it differs from other nitidulid larvae which have simple and generally very short urogomphi. The larva lives in oozing and fermenting sap and like the adult beetle is partly saprophagous and partly predacious. The breathing holes (stigmata) are located on conical, elongated processes, which serves to prevent their becoming sticky and clogged even when the larva is completely submerged in the fermenting sap. In the 1950s the very similar North American species, *G. quadrisignatus,* was accidentaly introduced into Europe. Within a few years it became established there and is now distributed throughout practically the entire continent. It is more warmth-loving than *G. quadripunctatus* and is found mainly in agricultural regions. In its native home it is occasionally injurious to maize.

2

The Nitidulidae family also includes one important agricultural pest — the Pollen Beetle (*Meligethes aeneus*) (1). It is an inconspicuous beetle about 1.5—2.5 mm long that nibbles the flowers and top parts mainly of cruciferous plants, above all oilseed rape and mustard. The larva is pinkish white with a soft body, only the head and the last abdominal segment are more strongly sclerotized and a dark colour (2); the thoracic and abdominal segments also bear small dark sclerites. The larva likewise nibbles the flowers and leaves of the host plant. Its development takes 3—4 weeks and

there are three larval instars. It pupates in the ground. The newly emerged beetles are active until late summer, hibernate in the ground, and may be seen again very early in spring, when they visit the first spring flowers (coltsfoot, lesser celandine, etc.).

141

C. cinnaberinus, the largest (12—15 mm) and most striking European representative of the Cucujidae family, is distributed throughout central and northern Europe, its range extending even into southeastern Europe and to western Siberia. However, it is a relatively rare species, which may be found only in unspoilt areas, mostly in mountain and submontane districts. The adult beetles, as well as the larvae, live beneath the bark of old trees and uprooted trunks, primarily fir, beech and poplar, and are among the greatest predators (particularly the larvae) to be found underneath the bark of old trees. The very shape of the beetle's body indicates that it is superbly adapted for living under bark. It is nearly as flat as a leaf blade which aids it in clambering through narrow cracks. This body shape is typical of most species of Cucujidae. The rust-coloured larva is likewise flattened and very active. The last abdominal segment bears two immobile processes (urogomphi) (1). In shape, coloration, movement and predatory habits it greatly resembles the larvae of the genus *Pyrochroa* of the Pyrochroidae family.

C. haematodes is another European species, one that is even rarer than the preceding species. It differs only by having a more rounded pronotum and in the red colouring of the mandibles. The adult beetles of both species are found under bark, most frequently in winter and early spring.

2

As a rule the larvae of practically all members of the Cucujidae family resemble the larva of *C. cinnaberinus* in body shape (1) and always have immobile urogomphi on the hind end of the abdomen.

The family also includes among its members some that are serious warehouse pests, i.e. pests of stored foodstuffs (e.g. *Ahasverus advena* and some species of the genus *Laemophloeus*). One of the best known is the cosmopolitan species *Oryzaephilus*

surinamensis or Saw-toothed Grain
Beetle (2), a pest of stored foodstuffs,
chiefly rice, flour and products made
from flour, which has been introduced
to all parts of the world.

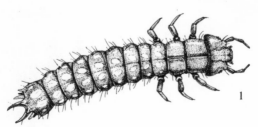

1

Raspberry Beetle
Byturus tomentosus FABRICIUS, 1775   Byturidae

The most plentiful of the three European species of the Byturidae family is *B. tomentosus*, distributed throughout the whole continent. It is found mainly in hilly and submontane districts but may also be encountered, though less frequently, in lowland districts. The yellowish beetles, about 3—4 mm long, may be seen in spring and summer on all kinds of flowers where they feed on the pollen. Since they have a thick coat of fine hairs they are often completely covered with pollen and are practically invisible on the flower. In May and June they mate on the flowers and 2—3 weeks later the female lays the eggs singly on the young fruits or flowers of raspberry, less often blackberry. She lays a total of 100—120 eggs over a period extending into August. The larva, which hatches after about eight days, burrows inside the young fruit. Commonly known as the raspberry fruit-worm, it occurs in large numbers and is sometimes responsible for the infestation of 100 per cent of the raspberry harvest. The larva (1) is pink and soft, only the head and dorsal plates of the thorax and abdominal segments are strongly sclerotized. The ninth (terminal) abdominal segment bears spiny, upcurved, sclerotized urogomphi. The larval development takes 35—45 days and there are three larval instars. The last instar falls out of the fruit and pupates in the ground close below the surface. The pupal stage lasts about two weeks and the newly emerged beetle overwinters in the pupal chamber, remaining there until May of the following year.

Another very common species — *Byturus ochraceus* — was also considered to be a pest of raspberries and blackberries. Recently, however, it was discovered that its larvae develop in the fruit of Herb Bennet (*Geum urbanum*). Adult beetles, like those of *B. tomentosus*, are found on flowers where they feed on pollen.

Related to the Byturidae are the beetles of the Erotylidae family, which live in fungi. Most of them are found in the tropical regions of South America but more than 20 species also occur in Europe. In the main they are glossy,

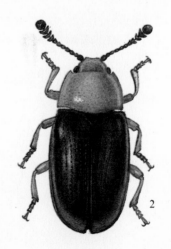

2

144

often brightly coloured beetles with an oval, greatly convex body. The largest European species is *Triplax russica* (2), found mainly on bracket and *Pleurotus* fungi. A typical characteristic is its black and rusty colouring. It often occurs in vast numbers.

1

C. dentatus is a small, 2—2.5 mm long beetle coloured rusty brown and covered with a thick coat of fine hairs. It is distributed throughout practically all Europe and Japan but, though very abundant, is encountered only occasionally because of its concealed way of life, a feature typical of most members of the Cryptophagidae family. It exhibits a predilection for decaying and mouldy matter such as the mycelia of fungi in rotting wood and under dead bark, old piles of animal excrement, rotting hay, straw, old foodstuffs, bird nests, wasp and bee nests, ant nests, old fruiting bodies of fungi, in short wherever the conditions are conducive to the growth of moulds. Adult beetles are not only found in but also feed on this mouldy material. They may be encountered practically the whole year round; in winter they hibernate. The larva is white and, except for the head and last abdominal segment, its body is sclerotized only very slightly and completely covered, but not very thickly, with long, erect hairs. The legs are short and slender and the last abdominal segment bears two short and blunt urogomphi. An interesting characteristic of all larvae of the Cryptophagidae family is that their mandibles are asymmetrical, the right mandible generally being furnished with a greater number of teeth than the left. Larval development is very rapid and probably includes only 2—3 instars. The pupa is also conspicuously covered with long to bristly hairs and has two long, slender processes on the terminal segment.

1

The genus *Cryptophagus* is a very large one. In central Europe alone there are about 60 species, some of which are pests of stored foodstuffs. Typical of all members of the genus is the toothed or otherwise notched edge of the pronotum which serves as a definite characteristic distinguishing the genus *Cryptophagus* from the other genera of the Cryptophagidae family. Some species, such as *C. lycoperdi* (1), live in puffballs where they can be found in large numbers together with their larvae at the end of summer.

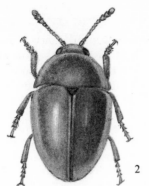

Members of the closely related family Phalacridae specialize in a different kind of food. For instance adult beetles of the species *Stilbus testaceus* (2) feed on grass rusts, as do their practically oval larvae that live inside the leaf sheaths of grasses.

2

Seven-spot Ladybird
Coccinella septempunctata LINNÉ, 1758   Coccinellidae

This popular, 6—7 mm long beetle is distributed throughout the whole Palaearctic region. Its markings differ in the various geographical regions. Apart from a few exceptions practically all European ladybirds are predacious. They feed on aphids, mealy-bugs, spider-mites, plant lice, white flies, and occasionally also on other small arthropods. The Seven-spot Ladybird feeds chiefly on aphids and is one of the most beneficial of all insects. In spring the female deposits the eggs, generally in small batches, on various parts of plants. This is followed a few days later by the emergence of colourful larvae without urogomphi. On each body segment the larva (1) bears several tubercles furnished with short, rigid bristles. It has relatively long legs and is quite agile in its pursuit of prey. Like the adult beetle it preys on aphids, destroying several hundred during the maximum six-week period of its existence. It undergoes four larval instars and pupates on plants. The pupa is mummy-like and the anal extremity is surrounded by the last larval exuvia. The pupal stage last 1—2 weeks. The newly emerged beetle is yellow, turning a darker hue and becoming fully coloured only several hours later. Adult beetles are active and hunt food until early autumn when they hide to overwinter in all kinds of crevices in rocks, at the base of trees, under bark, and even in human dwellings, mainly in cellars, attics and other unheated premises. In spring they resume their activity on the very first warm days.

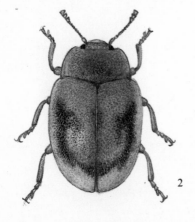

2

Observations have shown that the Seven-spot Ladybird also feeds on the newly hatched larvae of the Colorado Beetle. This also explains the presence of large numbers of its larvae on the foliage of potato plants. The Seven-spot Ladybird does not have many natural enemies for when disturbed it exudes a yellow, bitter and relatively caustic fluid from the leg joints which drives off many of its predators.

Some ladybirds, such as *Rhizobius chrysomeloides* (2), are small, a single colour and quite inconspicuous.

However, even this species is very
beneficial for it, too, preys on aphids. It
is very abundant throughout central and
western Europe and may be seen in
large numbers throughout the year in
the company of other ladybirds that are
not predacious but feed on the mycelia
of fungi and moulds.

1

149

Eyed Ladybird
Anatis ocellata (LINNÉ, 1758)   Coccinellidae

Measuring 8—9 mm, the Eyed Ladybird is the largest European coccinellid. It has typical markings on the pronotum and brick-red elytra with black patches edged with yellow. This species is distributed throughout the Holarctic region and is plentiful in all parts of its range. However it is more abundant in submontane and mountain districts than at lower elevations because it lives mostly on coniferous trees, mainly fir and spruce. There it feeds on aphids, chiefly of the genus *Dreyfusia*. The eggs are laid in batches on the underside of needles and on the bark of trees where aphids are present. The larvae hatch after 3—8 days (depending on the temperature) and their development, which includes four instars, takes about 30 days. The larva of the Eyed Ladybird is robust, about 18 mm long when fully grown, and coloured grey with prominent black and faint yellow and red markings. The tubercles on the abdominal segments are large, conical to spiny, and relatively inconspicuously hairy. The legs are strikingly long. The pupal stage of this species lasts 6—8 days. The newly emerged beetles are soft and faintly coloured and it takes a relatively long time for them to attain full maturity. This pretty and striking ladybird is also a very benefical species. Because of its size it consumes 2,200—2,500 aphids or their eggs during its entire development. Unfortunately thousands of these useful species die on adhesive strips which are used by ecologists to determine the population density of pest species, such as Black Arches Moth (*Lymantria monacha*) and Pine Lappet Moth (*Dendrolimus pini*).

1

One of the few phytophagous ladybirds is the species *Psyllobora vigintiquatuorpunctata* (1). It is quite variable and some forms are a single colour without spots. Some years it causes marked damage to alfalfa, clover and sugar beet. The eggs, coloured yellow, are laid in clusters on the leaves of the host plant and the larvae, which hatch a few days later, then nibble the epidermis on the underside of the leaf as well as the inner tissues. They do not consume the damaged plant tissues,

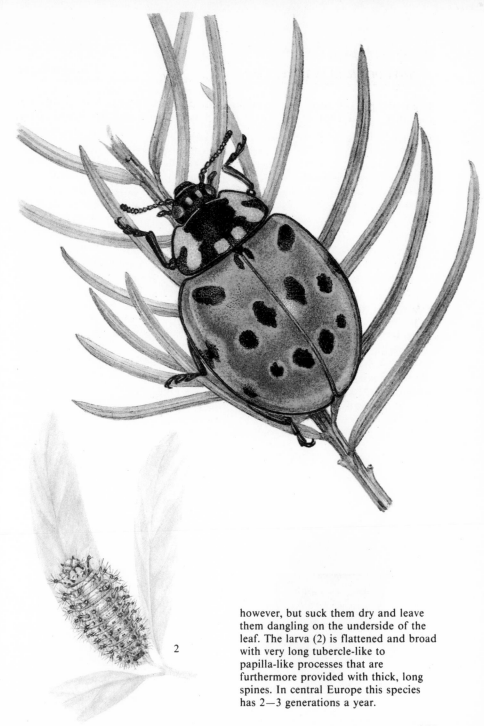

2

however, but suck them dry and leave them dangling on the underside of the leaf. The larva (2) is flattened and broad with very long tubercle-like to papilla-like processes that are furthermore provided with thick, long spines. In central Europe this species has 2—3 generations a year.

A. nodifer is a black beetle, only 1.5—2 mm long, with extremely interesting structures on the pronotum and elytra visible when viewed with a strong magnifying lens. In Europe there are some 64 species of Lathridiidae but this one can be identified at a glance by the large, smooth bumps near the tips of the elytra. It has a worldwide distribution. The beetles feed on moulds and the mycelia of fungi and are therefore found mainly under the bark of dead trees, in piles of old straw or hay, in compost heaps, bird nests, the burrows of mammals, and even in the nests of bumblebees, wasps and ants. *A. nodifer* has also adapted to life in man's dwellings and in warehouses. Here it is found mostly on mouldy foodstuffs, under old linoleum, in granaries, sawmills and in malthouses. The eggs are laid singly on the substrate that will provide food for the larvae, which hatch after 5—7 days. The larva is soft and white, with the body tapering slightly towards the hind end and without any appendages on the terminal segment. It is completely but sparsely covered with long hairs. Like the adult beetle it feeds on moulds and their spores. The larval development includes three instars. The last instar attaches itself to the substrate by means of a sticky anal secretion, remaining in this position for 2—3 days before pupating. When the beetle emerges the whole body is a pale colour, almost white, and it takes 7—10 days before it turns a darker hue. The entire developmental cycle, from the laying of the eggs to the emergence of the adult beetles, is very short (27—32 days) and thus there may be several generations a year.

Members of the Endomychidae family live in very much the same way as do the Lathridiidae. In Europe there are some 30 species, mostly small, convex glossy beetles. Some live in puffballs and are brightly coloured red and black, e.g. members of the genus *Lycoperdina* and *Mycetina*. The largest of the European species is the 5—6 mm long *Endomychus coccineus* (1),

which may be encountered in preserved forests, mainly in submontane districts, and whose coloration resembles that of a ladybird. It feeds on moulds. Another related but very little known family are the Merophysidae. All their members are myrmecophilous. *Merophysia striatella* (2) is found in southern Europe under stones, usually together with ants of the genus *Lasius* and *Myrmica*.

C. filiforme, measuring 5—7 mm, is a slender cylindrical beetle distributed in central and southern Europe. It is fond of warm places and is generally found on old, solitary and hence sun-warmed oaks. On such trees it seeks bruised spots devoid of bark (scars) which are generally riddled with thousands of round flying holes made by anobiids, scolytids and platypodids. The adult beetles are apparently predacious and prey on small xylophagous insects not only in their burrows but on the surface of the wood as well. They are active in the evening and at night and on warm spring and summer evenings occur in large numbers, scrambling agilely over tree trunks, chiefly on the aforesaid scars in old trees. In their pursuit of prey they worm their way through one anobiid flying hole after another, their slender, cylindrical body being eminently adapted to this way of procuring food. The larva is also elongated with a prognathous head and short sclerotized urogomphi on the last abdominal segment. Like the adult beetle it preys on the larvae as well as adult forms of xylophagous insects, chiefly anobiids and scolytids, and often also on the larvae of various wasps and solitary bees that build their nests in old tree trunks. It has also been observed that the larva of *C. filiforme* preys on bark beetles of the genus *Xyleborus* and is therefore a very beneficial insect.

1

Occurring in large numbers under the bark of dead trees are two predators of insects — the colourful species *Bitoma crenata* (1) and the flattened, soberly coloured *Cerylon histeroides* (2), the most plentiful member of the Colydiidae family in Europe. The larvae of both species likewise feed on small insects found under bark, spring-tails, etc.

The Colydiidae family is distributed primarily in the tropics and in New

Zealand but even in the Palaearctic
region one will find a number of species
that, albeit small, have a very interesting
body shape. The body shapes and
structures are many and varied, ranging
from long, cylindrical and smooth forms
to flattened, angular forms with very
complex and deeply sculptured
structures. Many species are also adapted
to a myrmecophilous way of life.

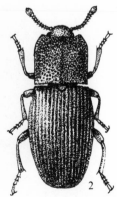

Mycetophagus quadripustulatus
LINNÉ, 1768

Mycetophagidae

The Mycetophagidae family numbers some 200 species worldwide; about 15 of these are found in Europe. They are mostly small and inconspicuous and live on fungi or moulds. The largest and most abundant is the 5—6 mm long *Mycetophagus quadripustulatus*. The shape and size of the orange patches on the elytra are variable and a completely black form is quite common. This species is distributed throughout Europe, its range extending to eastern Siberia. Generally it is found in large numbers on the fruiting bodies of bracket fungi, especially on *Fomes fomentarius,* but occasionally it feeds also on *Polyporus* species. The beetles feed on the spores of the fungi and on moulds and the spores of moulds and may be found from lowland elevations to high up in the mountains. They are reluctant to fly, but run very rapidly. The larvae are soft and greyish with the body tapering slightly towards the hind end (1). The last abdominal segment is terminated by two conical, sharp and strongly sclerotized urogomphi. The thoracic and abdominal segments have slightly darker dorsal plates. The larva's antennae are strikingly long and the mandibles are slightly asymmetrical. Its body is sparsely covered with relatively long, almost bristly hairs.

    M. quadripustulatus can be distinguished from the very similar *M. quadriguttatus* by the five terminal antennal segments, which are broadened. In *M. quadripustulatus* only the last four segments are broadened.

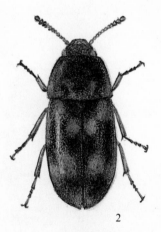

2

Litargus connexus (2), a 2.5—2.8 mm long beetle, is found throughout the Palaearctic region. This species is most plentiful in submontane woods and hilly country. The adult beetles as well as the larvae live in rotting mouldy wood and under the bark of dead trees, mainly beech. This species is very variable in pattern — not only in the shape, but also in the number of yellow patches on the elytra and thorax; completely pale yellow specimens can also be found. Until recently *L. connexus* was the only

1

representative of the genus *Litargus* in Europe. Several years ago, however, another species, *L. balteatus,* was accidentally introduced to Austria from North America. It has apparently become established and also now occurs in several localities in Czechoslovakia.

Cellar or Churchyard Beetle
Blaps mortisaga (LINNÉ, 1758)

Tenebrionidae

The Cellar Beetle is about 20—31 mm long, entirely dull black in colour, and with the elytra extending into a blunt tip at the hind end. When disturbed it adopts an unnatural rigid pose on raised legs and exudes a foul-smelling fluid from the abdomen. It is distributed throughout western, central and southern Europe, but nowhere does it occur very high up in the mountains. It is generally found in old cellars, barns and sheds or in dark, damp parts of old houses. It occurs less often in the wild, usually under stones, under rotten pieces of wood and bark, or in the burrows of larger mammals. The adult beetles are omnivorous, a characteristic of all members of the Tenebrionidae family. Because of their typical, penetrating smell, beetles of the genus *Blaps* have practically no natural enemies. The eggs are laid singly and are sticky on the surface so that they immediately become coated with bits of the surrounding material. The larva (1) is rusty-brown, quite strongly sclerotized and at first glance bears a slight resemblance to the wireworms of the Elateridae. The last abdominal segment is triangular, furnished with a short point. It is distinguished from wireworms mainly by the first pair of legs, which are longer than the other two pairs. The larva of this species, like the adult beetle, is omnivorous and lives in the same types of environment. The larval development takes up to two years and during this time the larva moults 10—13 times. The number of moults depends on external conditions and on the amount and quality of the available food supply.

1

The Cellar Beetle is the only species of the genus *Blaps* that has a preference for damp places. Other European members of the genus are typical steppe, xerophilous species, and many species outside Europe inhabit semi-deserts and deserts, particularly the Sahara and deserts of central Asia. All members of this genus have lost the ability to fly and have fused elytra. Most species of *Blaps* have the elytra prolonged into a blunt spine called the 'mucro'. In some desert

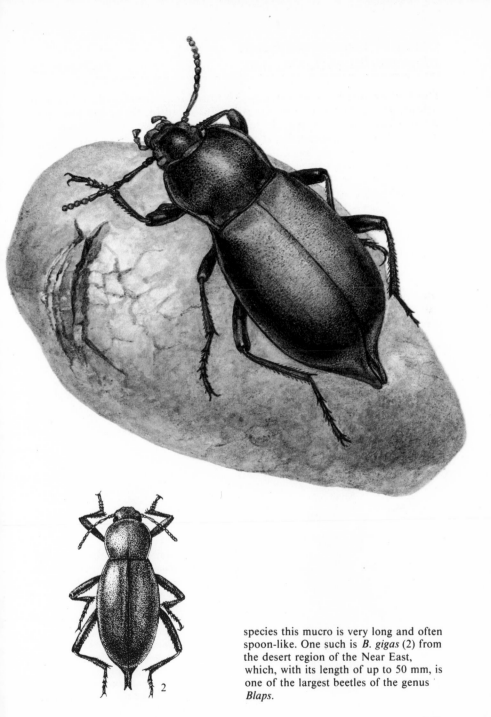

species this mucro is very long and often spoon-like. One such is *B. gigas* (2) from the desert region of the Near East, which, with its length of up to 50 mm, is one of the largest beetles of the genus *Blaps*.

Mealworm
Tenebrio molitor LINNÉ, 1758   Tenebrionidae

T. molitor is one of the largest and most serious, practically cosmopolitan pests of stored foodstuffs, chiefly flour and products made from flour. In the wild this 12—18 mm long beetle occurs, though only occasionally, in old hollow trees and under the bark of dead trees. It is often attracted to light and shows a preference for pigeon droppings in the attics of houses. The eggs are laid singly in the substrate on which the larva feeds. Larval development may take from several months to as much as one year depending on the temperature and moisture of the substrate. During its development the larva moults 10—16 times. The pupal stage usually takes 2—3 weeks. The larvae not only feed on products made from flour but also pollute them with their foul-smelling excrement. They are a yellowish or yellow-brown colour, cylindrical, up to 2 cm long and have two short, but sharp, urogomphi on the last abdominal segment. The larvae, known as mealworms, are also artificially raised on a large scale as food for cage birds, aquarium fish and terrarium animals. Because of their high fat content, however, they are not suitable as a steady diet for such animals; other foods should be provided as well. The larvae are also used in many physiological experiments.

Central Europe is the home of two other species of the genus *Tenebrio*, but neither of them has become a pest and neither exhibits any inclination to a synanthropic way of life. Both species are relatively warmth-loving and live in the crumbling wood of old, hollow trees, mainly oaks.

1

T. molitor is not the only species of the Tenebrionidae family that has adapted to life in granaries, warehouses and households. One of the commonest pests of stored cereals, flour, and products made from flour is *Tribolium destructor* (1) and its larvae (2). The larvae are whitish with two small urogomphi on the last abdominal segment. This beetle is becoming an increasingly serious pest especially in recent years. Its eggs and larvae are so small that they even pass

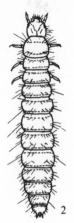

2

through flour sieves and are no easily seen. Furthermore the larvae attack not only products made from flour but also chocolate, dry smoked meats, dried mushrooms and fruit, herbs and spices and even pure cayenne pepper.

Diaperis boleti (LINNÉ, 1758)   Tenebrionidae

Found in the wild in central Europe are about 80 species of tenebrionids that exhibit a great variety of form, some of them not even resembling tenebrionids at all. One such is *D. boleti,* a 6—8 mm long beetle with an oval, very convex body, distributed in western, central and southern Europe and in north Africa. It occurs in warm localities from lowland to foothill districts and is tied to virgin or at least old stands of broad-leaved trees. Its bright, orange and black coloration is an exception among tenebrionids, which are usually a single, dark colour. Only occasionally does this species exhibit variations in elytral pattern; the arrangement and shape of the patches are usually constant. In rare instances, however, the entire front half of the elytra may be orange. The beetles live in tree fungi, usually bracket fungi, but may also be found in *Pleurotus* and other similar fungi. Often these beetles occur together in great numbers and can be located in the wild by their very strong, penetrating smell. They can also be found in rotting wood, because they can feed on the mycelia of xylophagous fungi. The larvae of *D. boleti* are yellow-white in colour; they have a cylindrical body with two small urogomphi on the last abdominal segment and resemble the larvae of *Tenebrio molitor.* Their development takes place in the fruiting bodies of bracket fungi, where the eggs are laid in spring either in small batches or singly. During its development the larva moults at least 10 times; the entire development takes one year.

1

The Tenebrionidae family numbers some 15,000 species distributed throughout the world, mostly in the tropics. They include beetles almost spherical in shape as well as ones that are long and cylindrical, beetles with convex bodies as well as ones that are flattened, and smooth-bodied beetles as well as ones with a richly sculptured surface. Some even have unusually large mandibles, e.g. the relatively common species, *Gnatocerus cornutus* (1), which lives in stored grain and occasionally damages products made from flour. The species *Scaphidema metallicum* (2) has a spindle-shaped body and is relatively common in warmer regions throughout

2

Europe. The adult beetles as well as the
larvae live in the mycelia of
xylophagous fungi. One of the
commonest tenebrionid beetles in the
wild is the conspicuously sculptured
Boletophagus reticulatus (3), which
develops in bracket fungi, generally in
whole colonies.

3

163

Omophlus lepturoides (FABRICIUS, 1789)   Alleculidae

O. lepturoides inhabits forest-steppe regions, mainly in southern Europe from Spain to Asia Minor. It is a conspicuous, 11—18 mm long beetle generally encountered on flowering umbelliferous herbs and shrubs, mainly hawthorn, where it feeds on pollen. In central and northern Europe this species is replaced by another very similar species — *O. proteus*. The beetles copulate on flowers in late spring and shortly after the female lays 200—300 eggs singly in the ground; their development takes 15—20 days. The larvae develop in the surface layers of the soil in sunny situations, often in the surface litter. They resemble tenebrionid or elaterid larvae, but are less sclerotized and the last abdominal segment is bluntly conical to rounded with very small urogomphi. They feed on decaying plant remnants. In some parts of southern Europe, however, *O. lepturoides* is a relatively important agricultural pest for the larvae damage the roots of alfalfa and potatoes in which they bore holes causing various fungi and bacterial diseases to develop. The number of larval instars is not known. The full-grown larva is about 3 cm long and overwinters in the ground at a depth of about 50 cm. It pupates in April at a depth of about 10 cm in an oval cocoon. The pupal stage lasts about two weeks, but if conditions are unfavourable the entire developmental cycle may take two years.

1

The Alleculidae are often regarded as a subfamily of the Tenebrionidae, from which they differ by the pectinate claws on the tarsi (the claws of tenebrionid beetles are smooth). Most members of the Alleculidae family develop in dead wood. The larvae of the species that live in wood are usually without urogomphi and feed on xylophagous fungi. The adult beetles are generally crepuscular and nocturnal, unlike alleculids that develop in the ground (e.g. *Omophlus*), which are active during the daytime. A typical example of alleculids that develop in wood is *Mycetochara humeralis* (1), distributed throughout practically all of Europe.

164

Also related to the Tenebrionidae
are the beetles of the
Salpingidae family. A typical
representative is *Rhinosimus ruficollis* (2),
notable for the prolongation of its head
into a long flat rostrum. It is common
throughout all Europe and is found in
mouldy, rotting wood.

2

Cardinal Beetle
Pyrochroa coccinea LINNÉ, 1761   Pyrochroidae

The adult Cardinal Beetle is scarlet, measuring 14—18 mm. It is distributed throughout Europe and in Siberia, occurring chiefly in lowland flood-plain forests and woodland meadows. In the southern parts of Europe it can be found relatively high up in the mountains. Adult beetles frequently visit flowers, because they feed on both pollen and nectar. Often, however, they can also be seen on forest vegetation, on tree stumps and on the trunks of old trees. The male is distinguished from the female by the finely pectinate antennae (the female's antennae are serrate). The eggs are laid in early summer in cracks in the bark of dead trees and tree stumps. The larvae, which hatch in about two weeks, are extremely predacious. They feed on insects living under bark as well as on their larvae, also on snails, earthworms, and, when the food supply in the immediate vicinity is depleted, even on younger larvae of their own kind. The larva (1) is superbly adapted to a predatory life under bark. It is flattened and very agile with a broad head and powerful, strongly sclerotized mandibles. The elongated last abdominal segment bears long, sharp urogomphi. In general appearance the larva greatly resembles those of the genus *Cucujus* of the Cucujidae family. This is a classic example of convergence where two totally unrelated species look the same because of the similarity of their way of life. The larval development takes 2—3 years; the fully grown larva can be up to 3 cm long. It pupates in a pupal chamber under bark in early spring and the pupal stage lasts 1—2 weeks.

2

There are only three species of pyrochroid beetles in Europe. The thermophilous *P. serraticornis* is the rarest; it greatly resembles *P. coccinea*, except that even its head is completely red. The third European species is *Schizotus pectinicornis* which, measuring 8—9 mm, is the smallest of the three but on the other hand the most abundant. Its pronotum is dark in the centre, there is a blunt, longitudinal ridge on each of the elytra, and the male's antennae are conspicuously pectinate. Its colouring is not such a vivid scarlet but rather yellowish-red.

Related to the Pyrochroidae is the Pythidae family, their largest representative in Europe being *Pytho depressus* (2), which is found mainly in pine woods throughout the continent. Its flattened larva (3) is likewise adapted for a predatory life under bark and in the cracks of dead wood and is most often found in old pine tree stumps.

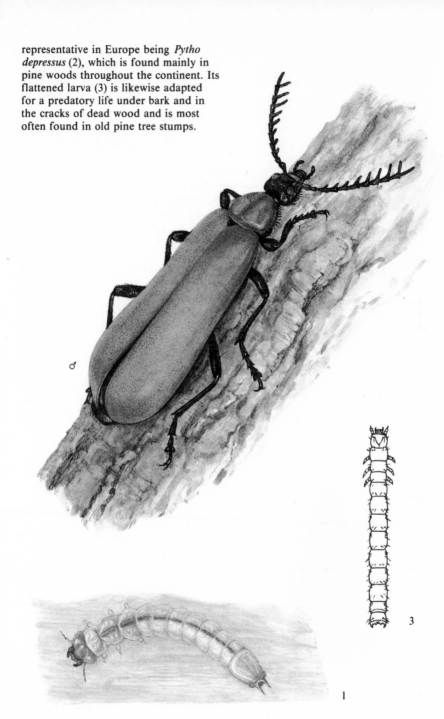

3

1

S. barbatus is an elongated, cylindrical beetle about 8—18 mm long, widely distributed throughout Europe and in Siberia. In southern Europe it is found only in mountain districts, whereas in the more northerly parts of Europe and in Siberia it occurs also at lower elevations. The maxillary palps of the males are broadly leaf-like and greatly enlarged, a characteristic of the entire family. The larvae of all other species of Serropalpidae develop in decayed and mouldy wood or in xylophagous fungi: only the larvae of *S. barbatus* develop in the hard, partially dead or dying wood of spruce or mainly fir. It can also be an occasional technical pest of wood. The eggs are laid in late summer into cracks in bark and dry hard wood. The development takes two to several years, depending on the quality of the wood and this also causes marked variability in the size of the adult beetle. The larvae pupate in June and early July in a pupal chamber just below the surface of the wood and the adult beetles emerge in July and August. The emergence holes are typical for this species — absolutely circular like those of some horn-tails, and infested trees look as if they have been riddled with coarse small shot. Adult beetles are active by night and are often also attracted to light.

1

The Lagriidae family, represented in Europe by only five species, is related to the Tenebrionidae and the two are grouped together into one family by some authorities. The commonest European species is *Lagria hirta* (1), distributed throughout the whole of Europe as well as in the Caucasus and Siberia. These are faintly sclerotized, soft beetles with a thick hairy coat. The larvae of this species (2) develop under the bark of old tree stumps and uprooted trunks or in crumbling, damp wood. The development takes one year and the adult beetles, measuring 7—10 mm, may be encountered on woodland vegetation, in meadows and on waterside growths. The tropics are the home of many large, often metallically coloured species of Lagriidae. The elytra of some are very convex, as if inflated.

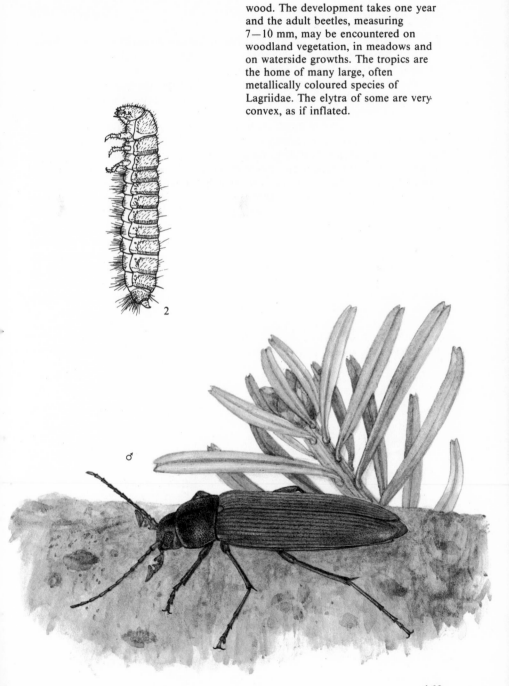

2

♂

Hoshihanonomia perlata (SUKER, 1776)   Mordellidae

The relatively small family Mordellidae is represented in central Europe by some 40 species, the largest of which is *H. perlata*, which measures 6—9 mm and is coloured black with snow-white patches on the elytra. It is distributed from central Europe through the whole of Siberia to the Far East, and is found in hilly and submontane districts. The elongate body tapering towards the hind end is only slightly convex above but on the ventral side it is very convex and keeled and the abdomen is terminated by a long, pointed tip. The legs are slender and long, the tarsi (particularly the hind ones) are much longer than the tibiae. On a flat surface *H. perlata* is able to move only on its side because of its keeled abdomen. In this position it also moves its legs back and forth very rapidly and prior to flying up in the air circles in spirals. It takes off with a spurt and is one of the fastest-flying of all beetles. Adult beetles may be seen on flowers, chiefly Umbelliferae and Compositae, and occasionally also warming themselves on leaves or tree trunks exposed to the sun. The eggs are laid in early summer into cracks in bark and in the dead wood of broad-leaved trees, mainly birch. The larva (1) is whitish and lightly sclerotized, only the orthognathous head is brown and sclerotized and sometimes the last abdominal segment is slightly darker in colour and bears short, sharp urogomphi. The legs are very short. The abdominal segments of the larva are slightly humped on the dorsal side. The larva takes one year to develop and pupates in the spring.

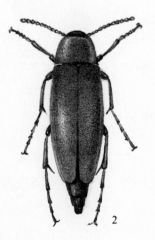

2

Most Mordellidae develop in dead, unrotten wood, only few develop in rotten wood. The larvae of some species (e.g. of the genus *Mordellistena*) develop also in the dried stems and roots of herbaceous plants. Until recently the Mordellidae family included several species that are now classed in a separate family — the Scraptiidae. These are chiefly members of the genus *Anaspis* that at first glance resemble Mordellidae but do not possess that family's characteristic abdominal spine. The species most common in central Europe is *A. frontalis* (2), which may be

170

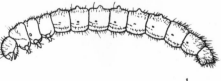

3

seen throughout the spring and early
summer, generally on umbelliferous
plants. The larvae of Scraptiidae (3) are
only lightly sclerotized and coloured
white with a brown head. The last
abdominal segment is long and oval and
covered with long bristles.

1

M. paradoxus is a beetle about 8—12 mm long with elytra that are slightly shortened, narrowed and spread apart at the tips. It is distributed throughout Europe and in the Caucasus from lowland to submontane elevations, chiefly in hilly country. The female generally has black elytra and antennae short-pectinate on one side. The male has orange or reddish-brown elytra and antennae long-pectinate on both sides. The development takes place in wasps' nests (*Vespa vulgaris*) and is a typical hypermetamorphosis. The eggs are laid in late summer into cracks in dead wood from which the wasps will take wood fragments to build their nest the following year. The first instar larvae, 0.5—0.75 mm long, called triungulins, hatch in early spring. They have long legs furnished with adhesive pads and are very active. They lie in wait for a wasp that will carry them to its nest. There the triungulin actively seeks a cell with a fully grown larva, penetrates it, and develops as an endoparasite inside the body of the wasp larva, where it grows very rapidly; during this time the wasp larva remains alive. Then the beetle larva bites an opening in the thorax of the wasp larva, climbs out, moults, and plugs the opening with the shed exuviae. Subsequently it winds itself round the thorax of the wasp larva and becomes an ectoparasite, biting another hole below the head of the wasp larva and sucking up the contents of its body. Then comes the second and soon after the third moult, during which time the beetle larva devours the whole of the wasp larva excepting the sclerotized mouthparts. It pupates in the cell of the attacked wasp larva, which the latter still had time to close. The adult beetles emerge in summer and do not feed during their brief life span.

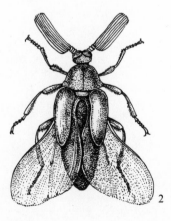

2

Though *Metoecus* is a parasite of wasps it does not cause much damage for it requires only a single wasp larva for its development. It is interesting to note that the beetles leave the wasp cell two days after the wasps emerge. Attacked cells in the comb can be identified at a glance by their paler colour and mainly by the flat operculum. Worldwide there are about 400 species of this family. As far as is known all live as parasites of other insects. In Europe the family is represented by five species; in central Europe, besides *M. paradoxus*, also by *Pelecotoma fennica* (1), whose larva is a parasite of anobiid larvae, and

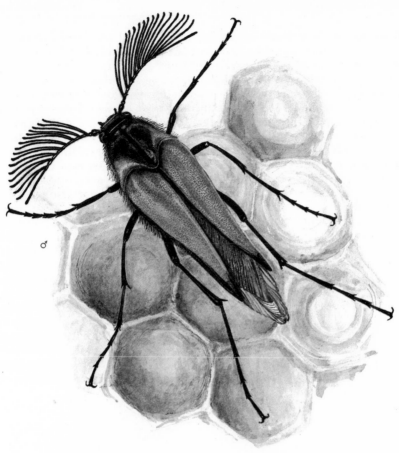

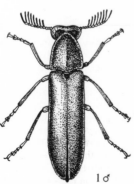

1 ♂

by the extremely rare *Rhipidius subdipterus* (2), whose larva develops inside the nymph of the cockroach *Ectobius sylvestris*. South European species develop in the oothecae (egg cases) of locusts and the nests of solitary bees.

M. variegatus measures 11—38 mm, is rainbow-coloured, and inhabits the warm regions of central and southern Europe. Typical of all species of the genus *Meloe* are the greatly shortened elytra, exposing the abdomen, which is generally smaller in the males. Adult beetles can already be seen in early spring in steppes and forest-steppes and on sun-warmed banks. When disturbed they exude drops of yellowish, poisonous haemolymph from various parts of the body, chiefly the joints of the legs, which serves to ward off and defend them from their enemies, particularly insectivores and birds. The life history of *M. variegatus* is a typical example of hypermetamorphosis. The eggs are laid in batches in the ground, just below the surface; during her lifetime the female lays as many as 10,000. The active larvae of the first instar (triungulins) (1) crawl up onto flowers where they await the arrival of a bee of the genus *Anthophora* or *Andrena,* to which they attach themselves and are carried by it to its nest. There the triungulin devours the eggs of its host, after which it moults and the second instar feeds on the honey stored in the cell for the bee larva. Once it has eaten the supply of honey the larva moults a second time and the succeeding instar abandons the nest of its host. After leaving the nest the larva moults, changing into an instar that passes into a resting period during which it does not feed but hibernates. In spring it moults for the last time, changing into an instar that is once again active and pupates. The very large number of eggs laid by each female guarantees that, because of the complexity of the ensuing development, at least some larvae reach full maturity and give rise to a new generation.

The genus *Meloe* is represented in central Europe by about 15 species. The development of them all is very similar and all may be seen only very early in spring, excepting the rare species *M. autumnalis,* which occurs in the wild in autumn. The species *Sitaris muralis* (2) has only slightly shortened but extremely narrow elytra. Its development takes place in the nests of solitary bees, built in steep loess and loamy banks, and it is in the vicinity of such banks or near abandoned sand pits or brickworks that this thermophilous,

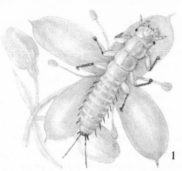

south European species may be encountered. Its development is similar to that of oil beetles of the genus *Meloë*, but the eggs are laid close to the nests of the host species and the triungulins make their way inside by themselves.

Epicauta erythrocephala (PALLAS, 1776)   Meloidae

Not all species of oil beetles have shortened or somehow modified elytra; most have normally developed elytra, even though less sclerotized than those of other beetles. One example is the genus *Epicauta,* distributed mainly in the semi-desert and desert regions of Africa and Asia. Reaching into Europe from the southeast is the strikingly coloured, up to 20 mm long *E. erythrocephala.* Its range extends from Iran and central Asia to the Balkans and even to central Europe. The adult beetles are phytophagous and locally are considered serious agricultural pests, particularly when they occur in large numbers. They nibble the leaves of cultivated plants, mainly potatoes, alfalfa, mustard, tobacco, cucumbers, melons, gourds, beans and others. Large infestations causing serious damage to crops have occurred in the Near East, where the beetles have destroyed 10 hectares of crops. Such catastrophic population explosions, of course, can occur only in the semi-desert regions of the Near and Middle East and central Asia because that is where the host locusts, inside whose egg capsule (oothecae) the larvae of *E. erythrocephala* live as parasites, occur in greatest numbers. These are chiefly *Gomphocephalus sibiricus,* locusts of the genus *Calliptramus,* and *Locusta migratoria.* In central and southern Europe *E. erythrocephala* is rare, occurring on various flowers. By no means do its numbers here reach such drastic plague proportions as in semi-desert regions, which are an optimum biotope for the host species of locusts.

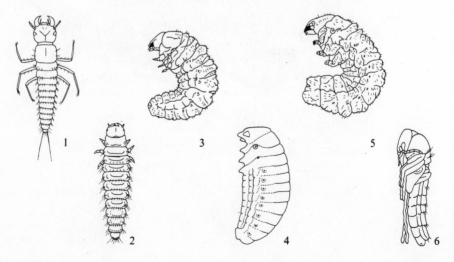

The eggs of *E. erythrocephala* are laid in batches in soil, immediately beneath the surface. The newly hatched larva of the first instar (triungulin) (1) actively seeks out the buried ootheca of the host locust and enters it. Then the larva changes into another active instar known as the caraboid stage (2), and subsequently into still another active instar known as the scarabaeoid stage (3). Then, after it has consumed the contents, it leaves the empty ootheca and excavates a side burrow where it passes into a quiescent, resting period and changes into what is known as the pseudo-pupal stage (4) in which it hibernates. In spring this pseudo-pupa moults and changes into the final instar known as the scolitoid stage (5), which is again active and which finally pupates (6). The adult beetles emerge from June to August.

Spanish Fly

Lytta vesicatoria (LINNÉ, 1758)

Meloidae

The Spanish Fly is a 12—21 mm long beetle coloured a vivid metallic golden-green. It is found in warm regions throughout Europe and in the east its range extends to central Asia, where it occurs as a very typical subspecies with a broad yellow band running the length of each elytrum from the base to the tip. The beetle's entire body contains a very toxic poison of the alkaloid group — cantharidin ($C_{10}H_{12}O_4$), which is dangerous even in very small quantities for it causes irreparable damage mainly to the kidneys. The elytra contain the greatest amount of the toxin and were formerly pulverized and sold on the market as a powerful aphrodisiac, but it is a dangerous 'love potion'. Until recently an extract from the bodies of these beetles was used in the form of various plasters. It has been proved that the extract from the crushed bodies of the Spanish Fly was a substantial component of 'aqua tofana', in other words the notorious poison of the Medicis. The adult beetles of this species are phytophagous and feed mostly on the leaves of ash, lilac and privet. When large numbers converge on a single tree they can strip even a large one bare in a very short time. As a rule in cases of such a mass occurrence their presence may be detected from afar by their penetrating, unpleasant odour. The eggs are laid near the nests of host species of bees and the triungulins make their way into the nest by themselves. Their development is once again the classic example of hypermetamorphosis with all the various stages that are present in the other species of oil beetles. The adult beetles emerge in late May or June.

1

The genus *Mylabris* numbers many hundreds of species distributed in the steppe, semi-desert and desert regions of the northern hemisphere and in south Africa. All are conspicuously coloured black and yellow or black and red as a warning coloration and the bodies of all truly contain effective poisons. The species *M. quadripunctata* (1) is distributed in central and southern Europe and in Asia Minor and its larval development takes place inside the oothecae of various locusts. Males of all species of the genus *Cerocoma* are noted for the bizarrely modified antennae.

2 ♂

Those of the females are only slightly
thickened towards the tip. The common
south European species *C. schreberi* (2)
develops in the nests of sphecoid wasps
of the genera *Tachytes* and *Tachysphex*,
where its larvae feed on stunned locusts
prepared as food for the sphecoid wasp
larvae.

179

O. femorata is one of the commonest European beetles and may be seen on flowering plants. It measures 8—10 mm, is a yellowish colour and is only lightly sclerotized. It is found in most of Europe except Scandinavia and extends eastward to the Caspian Sea. Favoured biotopes are warm forest-steppes and sunny banks at lower elevations. Adult beetles feed on pollen and are most often found on white flowers. However it is very likely that they also supplement their diet by sucking the sap escaping from bruised trees and shrubs. In both sexes the soft elytra taper off toward the tip, are separated by a slight gap and are slightly shortened so that the membranous wings are clearly visible. The male is readily identified by the conspicuously thickened hind femora. The females have legs of normal shape. The larvae of *O. femorata* develop inside the dead stems and roots of steppe and forest-steppe herbaceous plants; nothing is known about the number of instars. The larvae of Oedemeridae are white, soft-bodied and cylindrical, with only the head more strongly sclerotized and coloured brown (1). The last abdominal segment has no sclerotized appendages and is ony lightly sclerotized. The larval development lasts one year and the last larval instar overwinters and pupates in spring. The adult beetles emerge in late May and June.

The males of some south European species, e.g. of the genus *Anogcodes,* have thickened femora on the first pair of legs and some species also exhibit marked sexual dichroism.

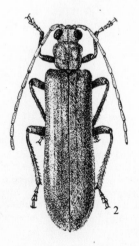

2

The great majority of beetles of the Oedemeridae family are active only on bright sunny days. One exception is *Calopus serraticornis* (2), which is a typical crepuscular species and is often attracted even to light. This elongate, 18—20 mm long beetle is atypical of the Oedemeridae, resembling rather some kind of longhorn beetle. It is distributed throughout Europe and Siberia to the Far East and is found on spruce trees, inside which its larvae develop. The adult beetle apparently does not feed at all. Because the larvae of Oedemeridae live only in dead wood or in herbaceous plants, they are not of great economic importance.

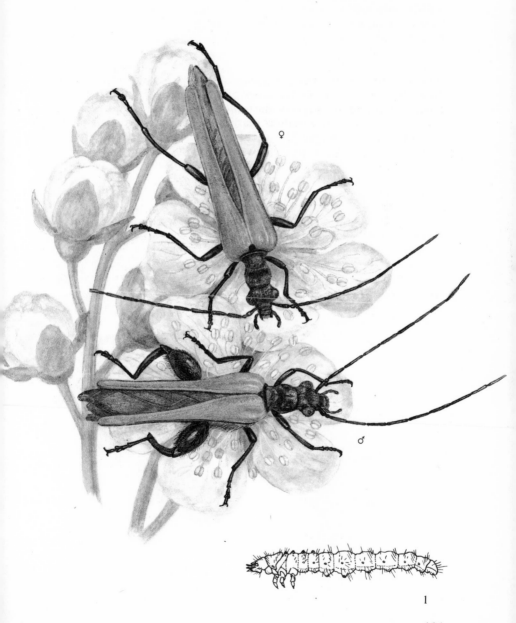

C. cerdo is the largest European longhorn beetle. It measures 25—55 mm and the male's antennae are longer than his body. It is found in old broad-leaved forests in warm situations at low elevations throughout the continent; only in the south of Europe is it found also at higher altitudes. The larval development takes place mainly in oaks but also in other broad-leaved trees. The adult beetle is phytophagous and nibbles the leaves of the host plant. When disturbed it stridulates very loudly (making shrill creaking noises) by rubbing the hind margin of the pronotum against the base of the elytra. The beetles swarm in June on warm evenings. During the daytime they remain out of sight inside their flying holes, under bark, or in the treetops. Often they also converge on sap oozing from bruised trees. The eggs are laid in cracks in the bark as well as on bruised spots. The larva, measuring 2—4 mm, hatches about two weeks later and begins to bore into the dead bark, reaching a length of up to 2 cm by the end of the year after the first moult. It hibernates in the bark and in spring continues feeding; by the middle of the year it makes its way into the phloem and the wood and often causes oozing of the sap in such spots. After hibernating a second time it finishes feeding in the middle of summer as a fully grown, 7—9 cm long larva (1). The number of instars is not constant. The larva bores deep into the wood where it excavates a hook-shaped pupal chamber. The pupal stage (2) lasts 5—6 weeks. The adult beetle hibernates in the pupal chamber and does not leave it until June of the following year. The development of this beetle is thus of three years' duration, but very often, because of the gradual drying up of the affected tree, it may be increased to as much as five years.

Most often affected by *C. cerdo* are old solitary trees exposed to the sun, mainly at the foot of the trunk. Further generations then make their way successively further upward. *C. cerdo* has many natural enemies, mainly various moulds and many parasitic species of insects, primarily Ichneumonidae and Chalcididae. Others include all species of woodpeckers and owls, which exhibit a predilection for this longhorn beetle during its swarming period. The damage caused by this beetle on old trees, mainly oaks, is twofold — physiological, due to the interruption of the tree's

2

1

conductive tissues, and mechanical, due
to the deep boring of many generations
in the wood, which is then totally
worthless commercially. The species is
rare in most of Europe and is now
protected in many countries.

Rosalia alpina (LINNÉ, 1758)   Cerambycidae

R. alpina is one of the handsomest of European beetles. It was found throughout central, southern and eastern Europe and in the Caucasus but is now known only in a few localities in Germany, where it is protected by law. This beautiful, velvety beetle, measuring 15—38 mm, is a typical inhabitant of the beech vegetation belt and is found at elevations as high up as 1,000 m. On the coast of the Black Sea it is found practically as far down as sea level, developing in hornbeam. Such localities, however, are exceptional. The black pattern on the elytra is extremely variable. In rare instances it is reduced, but far more often is expanded until in extreme instance the elytra are entirely black with only a pale patch at the base and a pale margin at the tip of each. The adult beetle is phytophagous, nibbling the leaves of the host plant and sucking up the sap oozing from bruised trees. The eggs are laid in cracks in the bark and wood of dying beeches. The development lasts several years (depending on the quality of the food) and the fully grown larva (1) pupates in a curved pupal chamber close to the surface of the wood. *R. alpina* is one of the many endangered species of beetles and deserves to be protected. In recent years its numbers have been rapidly decreasing in all localities, due primarily to the removal of dead but standing beech trunks and stumps, which is the only place where the larva can successfully complete its development. Beech stumps and trunks lying on the ground decay so rapidly that the larva cannot complete its development and is affected by all kinds of moulds and fungi.

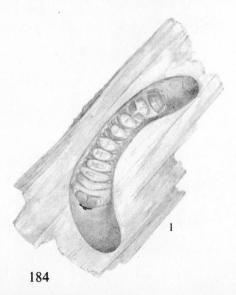

1

Stacked beech trunks in forests during the summer months also spell disaster for this species, for the female is irresistibly attracted by the freshly felled and sun-warmed trunks and lays the eggs there. The larvae that then hatch naturally have no chance when this wood is removed and processed. Unfortunately these beetles are also attracted to various pheromone baits put out to catch scolytids and subsequently die there in large numbers. *R. alpina* also has many natural enemies. Like *Cerambyx cerdo* it, too, is affected by many kinds of

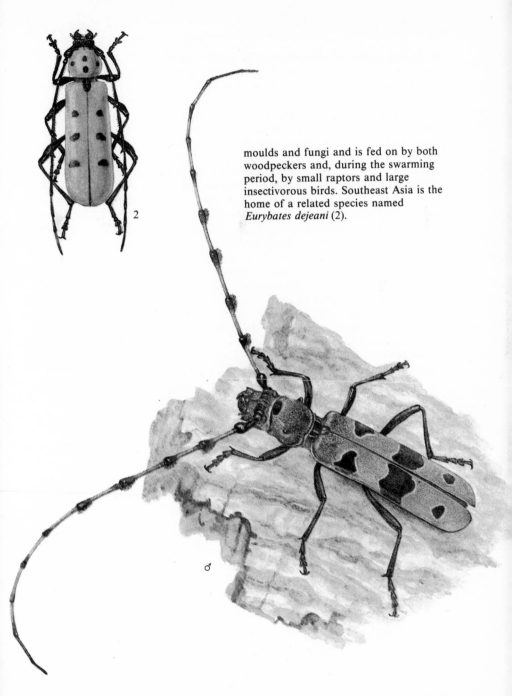

moulds and fungi and is fed on by both woodpeckers and, during the swarming period, by small raptors and large insectivorous birds. Southeast Asia is the home of a related species named *Eurybates dejeani* (2).

D. scopoli is by no means rare but leads a relatively concealed life and hence often escapes notice. This attractive, 10—13 mm long beetle is distributed in central and eastern Europe and in the Balkans, where it inhabits original and preserved steppes, warm, dry slopes and pastureland. Nowadays its populations are very isolated due to extensive farming. Like all other species of *Dorcadion, D. scopoli* is wingless and the abdomen is concealed by fused elytra. For this reason it is unable to fly and cannot spread from its separate, isolated localities to other places. Adult beetles run about nimbly on the ground during the hottest part of the day and feed by gnawing various plants, usually grasses. The eggs are laid in early spring in the soil right beside the root neck of the grass on which the larva feeds. The larva, which hatches after 17—20 days, differs from the larvae of most longhorn beetles by having short, well-developed legs. It feeds on the roots of grasses and is also suspected of gnawing the roots of sugar beet. Under normal conditions development takes two years; the number of larval instars is not known. The fully grown larva pupates in late summer of its second year and the adult beetle emerges 2—3 weeks later, but remains in the pupal chamber where it hibernates. The adult beetles crawl out of the ground the following spring and may often be seen on the very first warm days of April. The females of *D. scopoli* exhibit much greater variability in coloration than the males. This is true of all species of the genus *Dorcadion.*

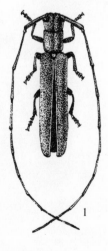

Worldwide there are more than 30,000 known species of longhorn beetles, most of them in tropical regions; in central Europe there are about 250. In terms of size their number includes veritable dwarfs approximately 2.5 mm long and on the other hand also the largest known beetle in the world — *Titanus giganteus* of Brazil, which is up to 22 cm long. The range of shape and colours is truly extraordinary, not only in the tropical regions but in Europe as well. One of the 'thinnest' longhorn beetles, *Calamobius filum* (1), is found also in central and southern Europe and its larvae develop in the stems of grasses.

The species *Molorchus minor* (2) is
notable for its greatly abbreviated elytra
so that the abdomen is freely covered by
the membranous wings. This species,
which is very plentiful in Europe,
develops in dying coniferous trees.

2 ♂

Rutpela maculata (Poda, 1761)   Cerambycidae

This 14—20 mm long longhorn beetle, strikingly coloured yellow and black, is distributed throughout Europe, in the Caucasus, Transcaucasia, northern Iran and Turkey. The black markings on the elytra are extremely variable. In some specimens the elytra are almost completely yellow with only the tip and a single lateral patch on each coloured black. In others, the elytra are almost completely black with only the shoulder area and two small patches on each coloured yellow. The male may be readily distinguished from the female by the hind tibiae. The female's are simple, without teeth, whereas the male's are slightly bent with two prominent teeth on the inside edge. *R. maculata* is a polyphagous species. Its larva develops in the dead, decaying wood of birch, oak, willow, poplar, beech, ash, hornbeam, hazel and chestnut trees. The female lays the eggs during the summer months, generally in trunks or branches lying on the ground, preferring wood lying in moss or some other moist substrate. The legless white larva bores and bites out its tunnels deep inside the wood, generally parallel to the axis of the trunk or branch. The larval development takes 2—3 years, depending on the nutrient capacity of the substrate and the altitude; the fully grown larva pupates in May or June in a curved pupal chamber immediately under the surface layer of wood. Adult beetles can be seen from May till August, mainly on the flowers of thistles and umbelliferous plants, where they feed on pollen. Even though *R. maculata* can be found from lowland to mountain elevations, it prefers hilly country and submontane biotopes.

R. *maculata* belongs to the large subfamily Lepturinae, whose members may be distinguished from other longhorn beetles by the body, which is generally slender, by the bell-shaped pronotum, and by the head, which appears to be constricted at the back behind the eyes. Another species of this subfamily is the south European cerambycid *Leptura fulva* (1). Even though its elytra are generally the colour of straw with a black margin, they may be entirely black with only a transverse yellow band in the shoulder area. The larva of *L. fulva* develops in the dead wood of broad-leaved trees.

1

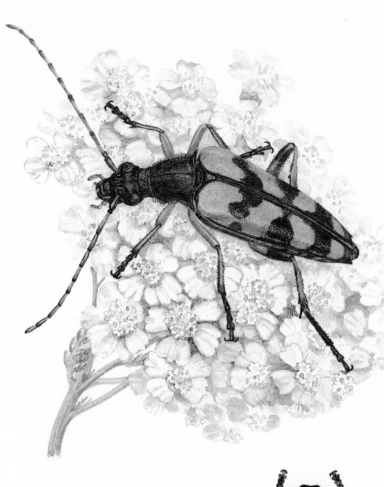

A classic example of mimetic
resemblance to a dangerous
hymenopterous insect, in this case
a hornet, is the species *Plagionotus
detritus* (2) found in the warm regions of
central and southern Europe. Its larvae
live under the bark of dying oaks.

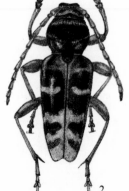

2

B. pisorum, an inconspicuous beetle measuring 4—5 mm, is a major pest of peas. Its original area of distribution is the region round the Mediterranean but nowadays it is found throughout the world wherever peas are cultivated. It is interesting to note that the eggs in the body of the female mature only after the female has fed on the pollen of flowering peas. The beetles mate at the end of May or beginning of June and soon after the female deposits up to 700 or more eggs on young, medium-size pea pods or ones that are fully grown but still soft. The larvae of the first instar, which hatch 6—12 days later, measure 1—1.5 mm and are coloured pink with a brown head; they have brown thoracic sclerites and well developed legs. These larvae burrow their way inside the pod by boring a long twisting tunnel in the wall of the pod until they come to the seed, whereupon the larva perforates the seed-coat and enters the seed. This whole process takes 1—2 days. Within the seed the larva moults and changes into a legless larva resembling those of the Curculionidae, which is very plump, devoid of bristles and thoracic sclerites, and coloured while (1). Only a single larva can develop in one seed. Further development takes 5—7 weeks. Prior to pupating the larva bores a circular hole from inside the seed, leaving it covered by only a thin membrane. The development of the pupa takes 20—23 days. In the climatic conditions of central Europe the adult beetles overwinter inside the seeds. In southern Europe or in heated warehouses they emerge from the peas already in autumn and overwinter either in the ground or directly in warehouses or households. The Bruchidae are good fliers and in spring they visit fields of flowering peas in great numbers.

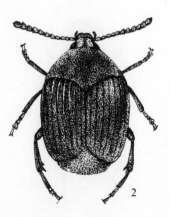

2

There are many species of Bruchidae that have specialized in feeding on specific kinds of plants (peas, lentils, beans, vetch etc.). One of the most harmful pests is the polyphagous *Acanthoscelides obtectus*, which attacks practically all kinds of cultivated vetches and may even have several generations in one year. It is probably native to South America but its distribution is

worldwide. In colder regions it lives permanently in warehouses or households. Small species of the genus *Spermophagus,* on the other hand, may damage ornamental plants whose seeds the larvae feed on. *S. sericeus* (2) is a plentiful species that develops in the seeds of *Convolvulus* and sometimes in species of leguminous plants.

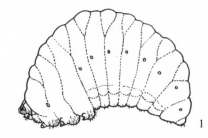

1

191

Donacia aquatica (LINNÉ, 1758)   Chrysomelidae

D. aquatica is a very handsome, metallic gold-green and purple beetle measuring about 6—10 mm and inhabiting a large part of Europe. Like the other members of the subfamily Donaciinae, of which it is a typical representative, it lives in the vicinity of water, on marshes and wherever the soil is permanently waterlogged. It is found on various aquatic plants including *Sagittaria* and *Glyceria aquatica*. In late May the female deposits the eggs on the submerged parts of the plants the larvae feed on. The whitish, eruciform larvae (1) feed submerged, boring holes in the plants with their well-developed mouthparts and, with the aid of the pharynx, pumping the sap from the plants into their digestive system. For purposes of respiration they make use of the oxygen in the tissues of the host plant by perforating the air spaces between the plant cells with the long, pigmented, hooked spines on the hind end of the abdomen and taking in air through the last pair of stigmata located at the base of these spines. In late summer the larvae pupate submerged, in the plants, in a cocoon filled with air. The beetles emerge in autumn but overwinter inside the cocoon and do not appear above the water's surface until late spring of the following year.

In central Europe the genus *Donacia* is represented by about 25 species, practically all of them feeding on a different kind of host plant. They are found on sedges, reeds, yellow water-lilies, white water-lilies and other aquatic plants. In most instances they are very similar, both in shape as well as coloration.

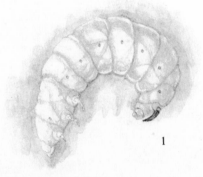

1

Thanks to the ingenious piercing equipment on the hind end of the abdomen the larvae of beetles of the genera *Donacia* and *Plateumaris* can live submerged and thereby utilize food to which most other phytophagous insects do not have access. The only exceptions are the caterpillars of several small species of pyralid moths that also feed on the submerged parts of plants but these usually obtain air in a different manner. A closer look at the spines at the tip of the abdomen (2) reveals that passing through them are channels via

2

which air is brought to the stigmata at
their base. The spines thus function like
a hypodermic syringe, to take in
air. Air either moves passively through
these channels or is conducted actively
by means of contractions of the insect
body.

Clytra quadripunctata (LINNÉ, 1758)   Chrysomelidae

Members of the subfamily Clytrinae, to which *C. quadripunctata* belongs, are characterized by a robust, cylindrical body, relatively long legs, and, as a rule, yellow and black markings on the elytra. The adult beetle is about 7—11 mm long and is most often seen on birches, alders, willows and poplars. It is distributed throughout Europe including Scandinavia, and the whole of Siberia including the Far East, where it is usually found in lowland and hilly districts; in the warmer parts of Europe it may be found relatively high up in the mountains. The beetles gnaw the leaves but never cause serious damage. The larvae live in the dome-shaped nests of ants of the genus *Formica* (mostly *F. rufa*) as indifferently tolerated guests (synoeketes). The fertilized female of *C. quadripunctata* deposits the eggs either directly at the edge of the nest or on neighbouring vegetation. When laying the eggs she envelops them in a case composed of a mixture of excrement and a secretion from a special accessory gland. The egg case, measuring about 2 mm and slightly resembling a pine cone, is carried by the ants inside the nest where the larva (1) hatches. The newly hatched larva does not abandon the egg case but merely adds on to and enlarges it as it grows and increases in size. The construction material is the larva's own excrement. The larva slightly resembles the grubs of Lamellicornia beetles and never abandons the case. It lives in the ant nest for 2—4 years, feeding on organic refuse and sometimes also on the ants' eggs. During the hibernating period and during pupation the larva closes the case with a plug made of earth.

The larval development of *Clytra quadripunctata* shows that nothing in nature remains unutilized, not even the refuse from ant nests. The larva of *C. quadripunctata* is of course rivalled by many other species of beetles, ranging from the Staphylinidae to the larvae of *Potosia cuprea*. The larvae of other species of *Clytra* live on the leaves of plants on which they feed, but even here they construct special, relatively hard cases which they never abandon throughout their larval development. One of the most abundant species is

2 ♂

C. laeviuscula which has elytra coloured orange with the dark blotches at the posterior end broader than in *C. quadripunctata* and often merging to form a transverse band. The male of the south European species *Labidostomis taxicornis* (2) is very exotic in appearance, has an enlarged pronotum and bizarrely prolonged front legs with widened tarsi.

195

C. sericeus belongs to the subfamily Cryptocephalinae, which is characterized by a shortly cylindrical, robust body and, as its name indicates, the head concealed beneath the front edge of the hooded pronotum. The elytra of some species are slightly shortened, thereby leaving the last abdominal segment exposed. *C. sericeus* is about 6—8 mm long. Its elytra have a metallic sheen but exhibit a marked variability in coloration; most specimens are metallic green or blue-green, but frequently one may come across individuals that are coloured violet, bronze or even azure blue. The underside of the body and the last abdominal segment protruding beyond the elytra are covered with fine, greyish-white hairs — hence the Latin name of the species. *C. sericeus* is distributed throughout Europe, its range extending eastward to Siberia. It is most plentiful in hilly and submontane regions but in some places (especially in the northern parts of its range) it also occurs in lowland districts. It may likewise be frequently encountered even high up in the mountains, sometimes even above the upper forest limit. Adult beetles are attracted to yellow flowers of composite plants, mainly dandelion and hawkweed. These beetles often occur together in large numbers, and thus there may be many differently coloured specimens on a single flower. When danger threatens the beetles immediately withdraw their legs and fall to the ground, where they may lie immobile for a long time feigning death.

1

The genus *Cryptocephalus* is one of the largest in the world with about 1,500 described species. Of these some 72 species are found in central Europe. Some are very similar, differing only in the structure of the males' copulatory organs and in their bionomy. Most species eat only a single kind or a few specific kinds of food. Their larvae live on the outside of plants and, as in the subfamily Clytrinae, are also enclosed in larval cases which are usually carried almost erect. Some move with a jerky

action. Most species are very colourful, generally with pale coloured elytra and dark markings, such as *Cryptocephalus quinquepunctatus* (1), which is quite plentiful in central Europe on willows and alders, and *C. vitatus* (2), whose larvae live on chrysanthemums.

197

Colorado Beetle
Leptinotarsa decemlineata (SAY, 1824)   Chrysomelidae

This beetle, a native of North America, was introduced into Europe in 1877, when it immediately began spreading widely. Up until World War I its main distribution was kept within bounds with comparative success, but in the period between the two world wars the Colorado Beetle invaded the whole of Europe and is currently even established in the whole of the European USSR and central Asia. It is merely a question of time before it colonizes the entire Palaearctic region. It is a relatively striking beetle, about 1 cm long, whose larvae live on potatoes where they feed on the green top parts. The eggs are laid in batches on the underside of the leaves of the potato plants, each batch containing 5—160 yellow-orange eggs (the average is about 30). Their development generally takes 6—12 days and the young larvae first of all devour the empty egg shell before beginning to gnaw out small patches in the centre of the leaf blade; only later do they begin to gnaw the leaf from the edge. The larva (1) undergoes four larval instars. The larval development takes 17—23 days, with the fully grown larva passing the last 4—5 days in a quiescent stage in the ground at a depth of about 3—10 cm, where it also pupates. It does not construct a pupal chamber. The body of the adult beetle remains soft for a relatively long time after it has emerged. There may be 1—2 generations a year, depending on the temperature and latitude. The adult beetle hibernates relatively deep in the ground.

The larvae of the Colorado Beetle are extremely voracious; the third and fourth instars may be responsible for the complete defoliation of potato plants. When they occur in plague numbers and there is not enough food they have been observed to resort to cannibalism. Potatoes are their staple diet, but the larvae may also develop successfully on other species of Solanaceae.

Phyllotreta undulata (2), of the related Alticidae family, is another serious pest. It is injurious to oilseed rape, radishes, turnips and various other Cruciferae, particularly at medium elevations and in rather damp districts. In spring the larvae as well as the adult beetles may

1

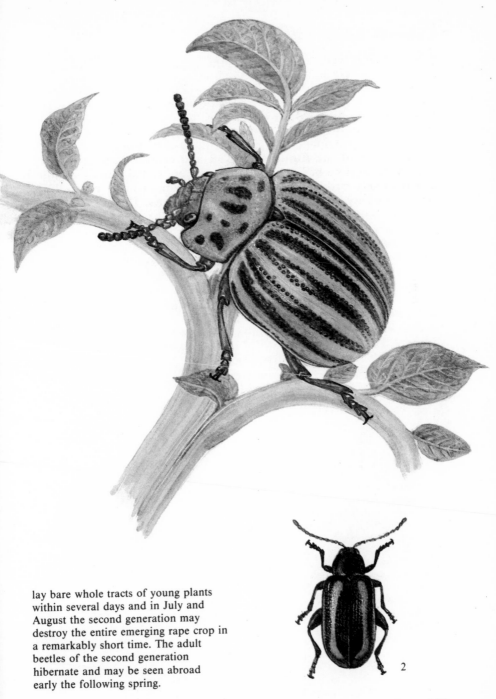

lay bare whole tracts of young plants within several days and in July and August the second generation may destroy the entire emerging rape crop in a remarkably short time. The adult beetles of the second generation hibernate and may be seen abroad early the following spring.

2

Timarcha tenebricosa (Fabricius, 1775)   Chrysomelidae

T. tenebricosa, measuring 12—20 mm, is the largest European leaf beetle. It is nearly spherical and greatly convex. Notable are the relatively long legs with unusually widened tarsi. This body shape is typical of species of *Timarcha,* of which some 100 have been described, mostly on the northern coast of Africa. The genus is represented in Europe by six species, five of these being found only in the central and southern part of the continent. *T. tenebricosa,* however, is distributed not only in southern and eastern Europe but extends as far as eastern Asia and even to Japan. It occurs in steppes and forest-steppes, where it is found on dry fallow land and in pastureland. This species has lost the ability to fly. The adult beetles as well as larvae are active only at night; during the daytime they conceal themselves under stones, bits of wood, moss, or in the detritus beneath the host plant, *Gallium mollugo.* Only on cloudy and cool days or after a heavy rainfall may the adult beetles be seen crawling about hesitantly even during the daytime. The larva has a soft, only lightly sclerotized body that looks as if it were inflated and is slightly reminiscent in shape to that of the Colorado Beetle larva. All species of *Timarcha* are dark coloured, usually black; only some have a faint metallic coloration. So far as is known the life style of all is the same, only the host plants are different. In the dry conditions of the Mediterranean region the same biotopes are inhabited also by some species of tenebrionid beetles, which exhibit a close resemblance to the beetles of the genus *Timarcha.*

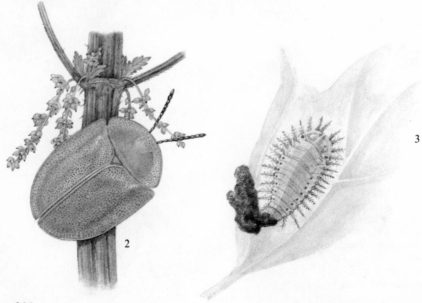

2

3

The subfamily Hispinae includes mainly tropical species of extremely bizarre shape, their bodies thickly covered with long spines. *Hispella atra* (1) is a common species throughout central and southern Europe; its larvae are leaf-miners of various grasses.

The large subfamily Cassidinae (tortoise beetles) includes some 3,000, mainly tropical species, some 40 of which are found in Europe. The lateral margins of the body are greatly expanded, which gives these insects a flattened, tortoise-like appearance with the legs completely hidden from sight when viewed from above. *Cassida viridis* (2) is distributed throughout the entire Palaearctic region. Its larvae (3) live on various composite plants. They are covered with long spines and on the terminal abdominal spines they carry remnants of old exuviae and excrement forming a sort of camouflaging shield.

1

The Anthribidae family includes approximately 2,400, mainly tropical species; only 25 occur in Europe. They are characterized by having the head prolonged into a short, blunt and usually flattened rostrum, slightly reminiscent of certain Curculionidae. Unlike the latter, however, their body is flattened and angular, the elytra are slightly shortened, and above all their antennae are non-geniculate. One of the largest European species is *A. albinus,* measuring 6—12 mm. The males may be distinguished from the females by the greatly elongated antennae. This species is found throughout most of Europe except the northwestern parts; it inhabits lowland and hilly districts with stands of mixed and broad-leaved forests. Adult beetles can be seen in late spring and during summer on the dead branches and trunks of old broad-leaved trees. They are not very active and, thanks to their cryptic coloration, resemble rotting, mouldy bark, and are practically invisible. When disturbed they immediately drop to the ground and feign death. The eggs are laid in dead wood infested by xylophagous fungi, on which the larvae later feed. The larva is legless, with body coloured white, unsclerotized except for the head and above all the mouthparts, and slightly curved in the form of a letter C. On the ventral and dorsal side of the thoracic and abdominal segments there are tufts of long, rigid bristles. Little is known about the development of the larva, except that it lasts at least two years and that pupation takes place in spring. Adult beetles are at least partially mycophagous, and associated with bracket fungi and the sclerotia of myxomycetes.

An unusual food specialization is exhibited by the larvae of the genus *Brachytarsus.* They live freely beneath the bark of broad-leaved as well as coniferous trees where they feed on scale-insects and plant lice (Coccoidea) and are hence very beneficial.
B. nebulosus (1) is a 2—4 mm long. inconspicuous beetle that occurs primarily on spruces, where it preys on *Lecanium racemosum.* It may, however, be encountered on other trees as well.

2

Anthribidae are abundant in the Asian tropics. This family includes not only veritable giants compared with other members of the family but also past masters in the art of camouflage and even in the imitation of other beetles. The Japanese species *Mecotropis ogasawarai* (2), for example, has such long antennae that at first glance it is readily mistaken for a longhorn beetle.

Beetles of the Attelabidae family are related to and resemble the Curculionidae but differ from the latter by their non-geniculate antennae. *B. betulae,* which is widespread throughout the entire Palaearctic region, can be a serious pest of grapevines and fruit trees in Europe. It also attacks birches, maples, alders, aspens, poplars, elms, lime trees and raspberry bushes. The first adult beetles, ones that overwintered in the ground, appear in late April and May. They feed for 8—10 days, first of all on buds and finally on leaves, in which they gnaw long stripes. After copulating several times the males die and the females lay eggs (4—10) in cradle-like rolls constructed from the leaves of the host plant. These the female makes by partly incising the leaf stalk so that the leaf wilts and remains dangling. She then rolls up these wilted leaves and cements the rolls with a viscous secretion. She always incises far more leaves than required. The eggs are deposited between the separate layers as the leaf is rolled up. The curled-up leaves soon dry, turn brown, fall to the ground and begin to decay. The larvae that have hatched in the meantime feed on this decomposing matter and are fully grown in 3—5 weeks. They pupate in pupal chambers in the ground, about 3—6 cm beneath the surface. The adult beetles emerge 1—2 weeks later but remain inside the pupal chamber until the following spring.

Whereas the adult beetles stand up very well to fluctuations in temperature and moisture, the larvae of *B. betulae* are quite delicate and a damp, cold summer or, vice versa, one that is very hot and dry, can destroy a large part of the population.

Brood care, typical of Attelabidae, is quite extraordinary. Various species roll up leaves in various, often complicated, ways (1). Some roll the leaves in a simple spiral, others change the direction in which the leaf is rolled several times, making use of various incisions and cementing in the process of construction. Some rolls are simple open-ended tubes, others are provided with a bottom, occasionally also a lid and various partitions. There also exist

2

instances of so-called 'cuckoo' species
that do not construct their own rolls but
deposit their eggs in the rolls of others.
Nature let its fancy loose in this family
also as regards body shape. The most
bizarre species is *Paracycnotrachelus
giraffa* (2), native to Madagascar.

1

The Brenthidae family numbers 1,700 species that are mainly tropical, with only one occurring in Europe. Bionomically the family can be divided into species that develop in wood or other plant tissues and species that are myrmecophilous. The single European species belongs to the latter group. It is *A. coronatus,* a 9—18 mm long beetle coloured rusty-brown and distributed in southern Europe, north Africa and Asia Minor. Adult beetles as well as the larvae are most often found in ant nests in rotting, moss-covered stumps but also in ant nests beneath large stones. The male can be distinguished from the female by the short, stout rostrum and the complex structure of the head. The female's head is almost smooth whereas the rostrum is long and slender. The larvae of the members of this family are relatively long and slender (1), lightly sclerotized, with a blunt to angular terminal abdominal segment, and usually slightly curved. The larva of *A. coronatus* probably feeds on various moulds and fungi, of which there is always a sufficient supply in ant nests. Pupation takes place and the adult beetles apparently emerge in autumn, for the beetles may be seen very early in spring. Species whose larvae develop in plants include many serious agricultural and forest pests. The females use their long rostrum, with mandibles located at the tip, to bore quite deep holes in plant tissues inside which they deposit the eggs. The larvae then bore tunnels of their own or else avail themselves of tunnels made by other xylophagous insects.

The variability of shape exhibited by the members of this family is enormous. In principle the body is always cylindrical and can be smooth or with very complex sculpturing; the hind ends of the elytra may be prolonged into long, straight or curved spines or else widened and spoon-like. The rostrum of these beetles may be short or long, thick or thin as a thread, but never curved as in the Curculionidae. The beetles are likewise extremely variable in size.

2

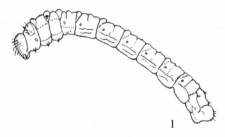

The related Apionidae family also
includes many important pests. One
such is *Cylas formicarius* (2); the adult
beetles as well as larvae are injurious to
sweet potatoes and to the tubers of
various tropical plants eaten by
native peoples in the tropics.

1

This 2.5—3.5 mm long, blue-green beetle is a serious pest of all leguminous plants. It is distributed throughout Europe eastward far into Siberia and occurs everywhere, except high mountain districts. The hibernating beetles may be found together in large numbers under dry leaves from autumn to spring, generally at the edge of forests, in hedgerows, etc. In spring they fly out from their hiding places on the very first warm days, visiting one newly growing host plant after another. The beetles are not fully mature at this point, attaining sexual maturity only after feeding their fill on the young shoots. They are not very active and at the slightest disturbance drop to the ground and feign death. Mating takes place in May and the females begin to lay eggs soon after. For this purpose they generally select buds that have not yet opened. The female first gnaws a small hole into which she deposits a single egg, repeating the process 10—50 times. The larvae, which hatch after about a week, are white with a brown head, legless, and with a short, plump, slightly crescent-shaped body. It is transversely wrinkled and covered sparsely with bristles. At first the larvae feed on part of the flower; later they crawl into the developing seeds. The larval development takes less than three weeks during which time the larva moults three times. The pupal stage lasts 5—10 days. The parent beetles begin dying when the new generation hatches so that the life span of the adult beetle is about one year. The newly hatched beetle is polyphagous and feeds on a wide variety of plants until the hibernating period, which begins at the end of September. Only after they have emerged from hibernation do the beetles begin feeding only on leguminous plants.

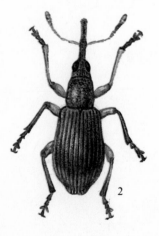

2

Species of the genus *Apion* are usually a single dark colour, occasionally with a metallic sheen. Differing slightly from this uniformity of colour is *A. frumentarium* (1), common throughout the warm regions of Europe, whose larvae develop in the galls on the roots of sorrel. A serious European pest of clover is the 2.2.—2.7. mm long *A. apricans* (2), whose larvae attack the base of the ovaries. There may be as many as eight larvae in a single head of clover, which make their pupal chamber

1

in the receptacle, thereby destroying
further flowers in the inflorescence. In
this species, too, the adult beetles
hibernate under leaves, moss, etc. In
years when they attack clover in large
numbers the loss in the seed harvest
may be as high as 20 per cent.

Large Pine Weevil
Hylobius abietis (Linné, 1758)   Curculionidae

The Large Pine Weevil is a serious forest pest distributed throughout the entire Palaearctic region. It measures 8—14 mm. After copulating a number of times the females lay their eggs (50—100) throughout the spring and summer in the bark on the roots of fresh stumps of older pines, spruces, firs and larches. The larvae, legless and coloured white with a brownish head, hatch after 2—3 weeks. At first they feed on the phloem but later they encroach on the sapwood, where they gnaw long surface tunnels filled with powdered wood. Before pupating they excavate a deeper pupal cell in the wood, plugged at one end with powdered wood. Sometimes the new beetles emerge as early as September and October, but most larvae overwinter and do not pupate until the following spring. Adult beetles live several years. In April, May and June they converge on the edges of woodland clearings where they mate. They cause the greatest feeding damage on young plants by gnawing the bark on the above-ground parts of the stem and causing extensive or smaller wounds. If feeding is more intensive the young plant is completely girdled with holes and dies. In July the beetles fly up into the crowns of trees at the edge of the forest, warmed by the sun, where they gnaw the branches. In autumn they descend to the ground, where they hibernate beneath wood as well as peeled-off bark lying on the ground and in forest litter. To eradicate this pest use is made of the fact that the beetles are attracted to fresh resin. The bait is made of two pieces of bark tied together, with inner sides facing, round a handful of fresh twigs. These baits are replaced after a week to ten days and are generally burned.

1

Another weevil that is a notorious pest is the species *Hypera variabilis* (1) which feeds on clover and alfalfa. Copulation takes place in late summer and the eggs are laid in September and October on stems or leaf-stalks. The eggs and some larvae hibernate. The larva (2) is coloured green, has rudimentary legs and on the abdominal segments pseudopods that serve as an aid in moving about on the plant. The larvae begin feeding in spring on buds and newly emerging leaves, in which they gnaw irregular holes. They hibernate and at the end of the following May, in their second year, they descend to the ground and pupate beneath remains of plants or mounds of earth, or burrow

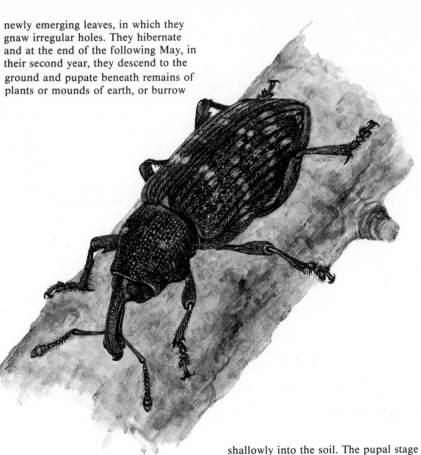

shallowly into the soil. The pupal stage lasts 12—15 days. The young beetles feed on the host plant and pass the months of July and August concealed under stones and amidst vegetation, after which they appear in September.

2

Magdalis violacea (Linné, 1758)   Curculionidae

The genus *Magdalis* embraces mostly secondary forest pests, i.e. the larvae develop in trees that are already diseased or damaged by other pests. *M. violacea,* measuring 3—4 mm and coloured entirely blue-violet, attacks mainly spruces, less often pines. In spring the female deposits her yellowish eggs in the branches of trees weakened by the feeding damage caused by bark beetles (Scolytidae) or longhorn beetles (Cerambycidae). First she gnaws a shallow hole in the bark and then deposits several eggs inside. The newly hatched larvae are yellow, legles and with a strongly curved body that is swollen at the anterior end. The entire head is retracted inside the thorax with only the mouthparts protruding. In general appearance the larva resembles the larvae of bark beetles. Upon hatching the larvae generally live gregariously and gnaw irregularly twisting, closely adjoining tunnels in the deeper layers of bark. Later they live separately and gnaw increasingly deeper in the wood. As a rule the tunnels run parallel to the longitudinal axis of the branch and look like deep grooves separated by high ridges. The larvae continue feeding until autumn, when they hibernate and later in spring pupate in a special chamber which they excavate at the end of the tunnel. Adult beetles live for several months and feed on the shoots and leaves of the host plant without causing any serious damage. One species of this genus, *M. armigera,* lives on elms together with bark beetles of the genus *Scolytus* and transmits the fatal Dutch elm disease.

One of the most serious pests of the weevil family, injurious to coniferous and mainly fir trees, is the 7—10 mm long *Pissodes piceae* (1) which attacks old trees from the roots up to the crown. The females lay the eggs in deep holes which they gnaw in the bark down to the phloem. The larvae bore winding, gradually expanding tunnels under the bark (2). That is where, under the bark between the sapwood and phloem, they also pupate in an oval chamber over which they construct a sort of roof of relatively thick and long wood chips.

212

Trunks attacked by this pest ooze resin
in many places, particularly next to
whorls of branches and old knots in the
wood. Adult beetles live 1—2 years.
Found in central Europe are eight
species of *Pissodes*, all of them
important forest pests of coniferous
trees.

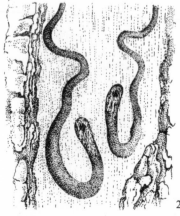

2

Weevils of the genus *Otiorrhynchus* are robust, slow-moving beetles with atrophied hind wings and fused elytra. Their number also includes several forest and agricultural pests. One of these is the polyphagous *O. ligustici,* which is injurious mainly to plants of the Leguminosae and Chenopodiaceae families and can damage sugar beet. It is distributed throughout the entire Holarctic region. Male beetles are extremely rare so that reproduction is generally parthenogenetic. *O. ligustici* is one of the few members of the vast genus *Otiorrhynchus* that are active during the daytime. The eggs are laid in batches of 20—60 in the ground, at a depth of 2—5 cm, in the vicinity of the plant the larvae feed on. They may be deposited over a period of up to three months and their development takes 2—3 weeks. The newly hatched larvae feed on the root necks of the young plants at first but later they burrow deeper into the ground and feed on the plant roots, devouring thin rootlets completely and in the case of stronger roots gnawing 2—5 mm wide passages which they fill with powdered wood and excrement. They overwinter in oval chambers in the ground, at a depth of 5—75 cm. Fully grown larvae remain inside the chambers until June of the following year and pupate there. Immature larvae continue feeding in spring and overwinter a second time. The larval stage includes seven instars. The pupal stage lasts 20—30 days. Thanks to the fact that two years (in uncongenial conditions as much as three years) are required for the beetles' development, it cannot take place on annual plants.

1

Weevils of the genus *Curculio* are characterized by their extremely long, slender 'snout'. The Nut Weevil (*C. nucum*) (1) lives on hazels and oaks and during the feeding period damages the leaves and young fruits which are then attacked by moulds. When laying eggs the female first drills a deep hole in the nut, deposits the egg on the edge, and then pushes it to the very bottom of the hole with her long snout. 8—10 days later, when the opening is already scarred over, the larva hatches, causing

the formation of a sort of gall on which
it first feeds; later it feeds on the kernel
until that has been consumed and only
larval excrement is left inside the nut. In
the autumn the larva (2) bores a hole in
the nutshell, drops to the ground, buries
itself in the soil (as much as 25 cm
deep) and pupates in a firm chamber.
The adult beetle does not emerge until
late the following spring.

2

Spruce Bark or Engraver Beetle
Ips typographus (LINNÉ, 1758)   Scolytidae

The damage caused by the Spruce Bark Beetle in spruce stands can be very serious; only a forest fire might possibly be worse. Except for the Iberian Peninsula, this 4.2—5.5 mm long beetle is distributed throughout the entire Palaearctic region. The beetles begin swarming as early as the first week of May, in mountain districts not until June. The male visits a suitable tree and bores a 'nuptial chamber' in the bark. 1—2 days later the females, usually two, arrive in the chamber where copulation takes place. Then each female begins excavating a separate individual gallery, always in the vertical direction — one (or two) upward and one (or two) downward. On either side of the gallery the female makes a number of notches in which she deposits a single egg. Each female thus prepares the foundations for 20—100 lateral tunnels. The larvae, which hatch after 5—14 days, are white with a brown head and unsclerotized body curved in the form of a crescent (1). During its development, which takes 26—113 days depending on the temperature, the larva moults 4—5 times. It bores in the phloem and gnaws a lateral tunnel at right angles to the main gallery made by the female. The larval tunnel is about 6 cm long, slightly wavy and broader at the end. The entire engraving (2) is very typical and cannot be mistaken for one made by any other bark beetle. The larval tunnel is terminated by a broadened pupal chamber. The entire development takes 7—10 weeks (in the non-hibernating generation), and generally there are two generation in one year. The newly emerged beetles must feed for three weeks before attaining full maturity.

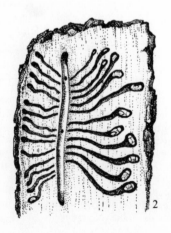

The best conditions for the development of the Spruce Bark Beetle are provided by stands damaged by gales or snow. In such areas the beetle exhibits a preference for uprooted trees or pieces of a tree trunk lying on the ground. The next generation generally still finds ample places suitable for development in trees leaning over after gales where the roots may have been damaged. When the second generation has completed its development, however, the food supply in the devastated area is no longer sufficient for the enormous number of beetles and so they launch

a destructive attack on healthy trees, mainly those on the margin of the devastated area. From there the infestation usually spreads in belts until entire stands are infested. The most effective means of controlling the Spruce Bark Beetle is the timely clearing of such areas and the burning of peeled bark.

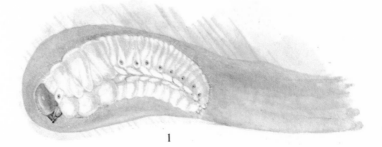

1

Pityokteines curvidens (GERMAR, 1824)   Scolytidae

This species is also an important forest pest, particularly of Silver Fir. It measures 2.5—3 mm with its cylindrical body coloured rusty-brown and the elytra characteristically toothed at the tip. The beetles swarm in March and April. As a rule 3—4 main galleries branch from the nuptial chamber, generally in the horizontal direction, so that the engraving looks like a capital letter I with large, long cross-bars. The larval tunnels are quite short, ending under thin bark in pupal cells located in the bark. July sees the appearance of the second generation. The newly emerged adult beetles bore into the bark of healthy trees on the edge of the forest to hibernate and the trunks are then conspicuously marked with oozing resin. In addition to this the larvae and pupae of the second and possible third generation also hibernate. At high elevations there is only one generation a year. *P. curvidens* attacks first at the forest's edge or in thin stands. Shaded trees in a dense stand are usually spared. Along with atmospheric pollution, this pest is one of the main causes of the recent mass dying of fir trees all over Europe. The further danger presented by all bark beetles is that even in trees infested only in small measure by these beetles they bring with them all sorts of mould and fungal infections that contribute to the death of the trees. However, they have a number of natural enemies. Chief among these are the larvae of Staphylinidae, Histeridae, Nitidulidae and Raphidioptera. Also many hymenopterous insects are parasites of bark beetle larvae.

1

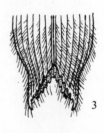

3

Until recently the Platypodidae were classed as a subfamily of the Scolytidae, but they are now classed as a separate family albeit one that is very closely related to the Scolytidae. *Platypus cylindrus* (1) causes damage mainly to

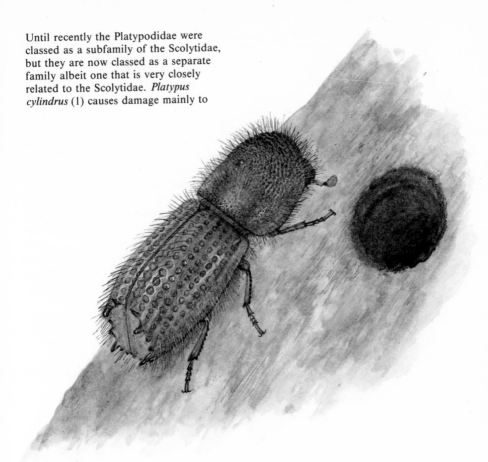

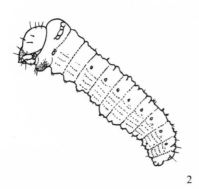

2

oak wood. The beetles swarm in July and attack damaged tree trunks at the base. The larva (2), white, cylindrical and practically glabrous, bores tunnels circular in cross-section to a depth of 15 cm, shoving out relatively coarse wood shavings whereby it differs from the larvae of bark beetles. This species will very occasionally also attack beech, elm and ash trees. The other species of this family found in Europe differs conspicuously in the shape of the elytra at the tip. Whereas the elytra of *P. cylindrus* are bluntly rounded at the tip (1), those of *P. oxyurus* are prolonged into two long spines (3).

INDEX

(Numbers in bold refer to main entries, numbers in italics to illustrations)

221